Autistic or Toxic?

*How I Unlocked the Mystery
of My Son's "Autism"*

Scarlett South

White Sands Publications

Autistic or Toxic?
How I Unlocked the Mystery of My Son's "Autism"
by Scarlett South

Published by

White Sands Publications
whitesandspublications@gmail.com

Cover and interor layout: NZ Graphics

ISBN: 978-1-7349890-0-7 (print)
ISBN: 978-1-7349890-1-4 (eBook)

First Edition

Printed in the United States of America

Contents

Preface

Things haven't changed much in the world of autism in the twenty-some years since my son, Luke, was diagnosed with the condition, except that the numbers have skyrocketed since then; 1 in 54 I read somewhere, as opposed to around 1 in 2500 when my son was born in the early nineties. The experts still don't know what causes autism, and there still isn't a cure for this mysterious disorder.

Though there is no magic cure-all, there are measures we can take to lessen our child's autistic tendencies, thus steering them towards a future as an independent adult. I want to share with you what I have learned through the years of heartache, as well as triumph, as I ventured with my son down that elusive road toward autism recovery. Though I stumbled along the way as I blindly navigated the myriad treatments and latest miracle "cures," in hindsight, the path was crystal-clear.

The treatments that got Luke well may not work for every child with autism, as there are many subsets of autism. So please, see a medical provider before embarking on any treatments in my book. I am in no way a medical doctor, but I am the mom of a child who was once labeled as being severely autistic, with talk of being placed in an institution. I tried everything the traditional doctors recommended, but Luke did not respond well to their treatments. It took blazing a trail into unknown territory before Luke began to emerge as a typically-developing child.

But keeping him that way was a challenge onto itself.

I spent two years researching this book before I ventured into writing it, with the hopes and dreams of helping children with autism flourish into independent adults, which, in my mind, is recovery from autism. By reading this book, you'll be able to avoid the mistakes I made, as well as the expenses I incurred while making those mistakes, so that you, as the parent or guardian of a child with autism, will be wiser as you navigate your own path down that mysterious road called autism.

I will forever be grateful to Luke for coming into my life. Even in our darkest days, he has enriched my life, and given me the purpose I so desperately craved. Also, a special heartfelt acknowledgement to his twin in heaven; for if it weren't for him, Luke would not be where he is today … a happy and healthy, independent and productive member of society!

Scarlett

Chapter 1

Luke was a mystery, an enigma that baffled doctors from the time he was thrust into our world, hastened in his birth by his dying twin. The doctors scrambled to save them, and managed to keep Luke alive with the help of a breathing machine.

But his twin was too badly damaged. He weighed two pounds, and his skin had a gray pallor. With bowed heads, the doctors circled my husband and I as we hovered over our baby's incubator, hands clasped, and told us that his outlook was bleak. Our baby had a grade-four bleed in his brain, they explained, which would have required surgery to put in a shunt. He also had a hole in his heart that would have required open-heart surgery to repair it, and the lumen in his large intestine was closed, which would have required major surgery to open it.

"The only compassionate thing to do is to let him go," the doctor in charge of the neonatal ICU said in a gentle voice. "He's just too sick to survive all of these surgeries."

My husband and I clung to each other, and could only nod in mute assent. The doctor removed my baby from the machines that had kept him alive and placed him in my arms. Tears coursed down my cheeks as I kissed my baby one last time, then cuddled him as he took his last breath and became still.

I looked up at the doctor and sobbed, "What killed my baby?"

The doctor pushed a lock of white hair from his eyes and spread his hands in a gesture of defeat. "It's a mystery to us. We've never seen anything like this. His part of the placenta was in shreds, and we don't know what caused that. The discrepancies in their weights indicates a disease process; we just don't know which one it is, though. We thought that maybe you had passed a virus onto him; CMV to be specific, but we tested him for that, and he tested negative."

Three days later, we had just buried our baby when the doctor called. "Good news," he chortled. "We took Luke off the ventilator this morning, and he's breathing room air without any difficulty. We're just going to give him his vaccine, and then you can come and get him."

I felt my spine stiffen as the breath got caught in my throat. "*Vaccine!*" I bellowed. "What are you giving him a vaccine for already? Isn't he too tiny and too sick for a vaccine? He's only four pounds, you know, and just now breathing on his own. Wouldn't a vaccine, full of God-knows-what, be too much of a burden for his tiny body?"

The doctor's chuckle reverberated through the phone line. "No need to worry. It's 1992. Vaccines are *harmless*. And, besides, they're required by law for every newborn, regardless of state of health. Now come get your baby and take him home."

The sun was sinking behind a silhouette of pine trees when we pulled up in our yard, bathing the cotton fields that stretched to the foothills of the Blue Ridge mountains in a palette of dusty pink and lavender. Our home had been a relic of the Civil War, an Antebellum homestead with sagging floorboards and peeling paint. Behind the house, a barn stacked with rusting canisters of fertilizer and pesticides that farmers had sprayed the fields with, leaned precariously over an old black well, which we used for our drinking and cooking water.

Just as we had alit from the car a plane flew over our heads, showering the fields with chemicals. A breeze ruffled my hair, damp with moisture from the hot, humid air. As I removed Luke from his car seat, I instinctively covered my baby's face with his blanket as I bundled him in my arms, shielding him from particles that rained upon us.

I felt my brow crease as I stared at the taillights of the waning plane, then turned to my husband. "Are you sure it's safe for Luke, living here surrounded by all of these chemicals?"

Gary, my husband, a tall, slim man with black hair and dark skin that hinted at his Italian heritage, scowled at me. "How many times do you keep asking me that same tired question? And, how many times do I have to tell you the same thing over and over and *over* again? You and Luke are absolutely safe here. I'm a doctor, for God's sake. Don't you trust me enough to know what I'm talking about?"

He lowered his voice until it became a velvety croon, then draped an arm around my shoulders, pulling Luke and I against the comfort of his chest. "Come on, baby. Do you actually think that I would put you and our baby in harm's way?"

My shoulders sagged and I shook my head, caving into the power of my husband's charm, once again. "No," I whispered, "I have faith in you."

Gary had fallen in love with the decrepit old house upon crossing its crumbling threshold, insisting on buying it and restoring it to its former glory. We, or should I say I, scraped faded wallpaper off the walls and sanded layers of paint that had withstood the test of time for more than a century, gagging and choking on clouds of dust.

It was shortly after I had applied the last layer of paint that I found out that I was pregnant with twins ….

Chapter 2

The signs of autism were apparent in Luke from the moment we brought him home from the hospital. I didn't have any clue as to what was going on with him, though, since autism back then wasn't nearly as prevalent as it is now. He didn't babble and coo like other babies, and would become stiff as the proverbial board, shifting his eyes to avoid my gaze, when I tried to cuddle him.

Since I worked with my husband in his office, managing his practice, I was able to take Luke to work with me. I had set up a swing next to my desk that I would put Luke in while I did my tasks, my baby content to rock the day away staring into space, his hands clenched into tiny fists.

When bedtime came, Luke didn't sleep. Instead, he would mewl deep into the night, which drove me into a sleep-deprived psychosis. As ashamed as I am to say this, I had to awaken my husband one night and thrust Luke into his arms. I told him that I was about to hurt our baby if he didn't take him and let me sleep.

At Luke's two-week check-up, he weighed less than his birth weight of four pounds. His pediatrician, a displaced French-Canadian with a head full of untamed curls, looked at the scales, then turned to me with terror blazing from his eyes as he placed Luke in my arms.

"Oh dear, oh dear," the doctor exclaimed in a thick French accent, wringing his hands.

"What's wrong?" I cried, clutching Luke.

The doctor pinned me with his piercing blue eyes. "Madam, I'm sorry to be the bearer of bad news, but your baby is a failure-to-thrive baby, and needs to go to the hospital immediately, or he will die."

I started trembling as tears flooded my eyes. "What are you saying? How is he failure-to-thrive?" I shrieked.

"Your baby is losing too much weight," the doctor explained, "and, that's not normal."

He looked down at Luke and frowned. "His skin is pasty and he's sweating. We need to get him into the hospital so that they can force-feed him high-calorie formula."

"How are they going to do that?" I asked.

"They'll put a tube through his nose and into his stomach," the doctor replied.

I looked down at my baby and shuddered, then lifted my gaze to the doctor. "Look. Luke's been through enough, already, without having tubes shoved up his nose. I'm a registered nurse. My husband is an Internal Medicine doctor. Why can't I just do it at home myself instead of dragging him into another hospital? He swallows well enough, so it shouldn't be that difficult. And if he doesn't gain weight doing it my way, *then* we can put him in the hospital."

"What do you think?" I asked, then held my breath as I awaited the doctor's answer.

"I think you're *nuts*," the doctor blurted out. "But since your husband's a highly-esteemed doctor in our community, and you're a nurse, your baby should be in good hands. But, if God forbid, something bad does happen, you get him to the emergency room, pronto!"

The doctor grunted as I nodded my understanding, then dashed out of the exam room as if the place was on fire. He returned a few minutes later lugging a case of formula. "This here is the best formula on the market for failure-to-thrive babies," he said. "It's highly concentrated, with extra milk and fat to add calories."

The doctor handed me the formula. "Come back in a week. If your baby hasn't gained any weight by then, then we're going to have him admitted to the hospital."

I started Luke on the formula as soon as we got home. Within the next few days, a rosy hue crept into his cheeks, and he appeared to be a little plumper.

After about a week of starting the formula, Luke developed a constant sniffle, and a clear drainage leaked from his nose. He started yanking on his tiny ears and screaming, his wails shattering the still of the night. I rocked him and paced the hallways with him until I thought I would go mad from sleep deprivation. But nothing I did would solace him.

At Luke's next check-up, the doctor placed him on the scales, then threw up his hands and cried, "He's out of the woods!" as if he had just placed the healing hands on my baby.

I couldn't help but laugh at his theatrics, then took on a sobering tone as I took my baby from the doctor and cradled him in my arms. "It's great that we got his weight up, but he's developed allergies, and I'm afraid his ears are infected."

The doctor looked inside Luke's ears with an otoscope and announced that, indeed, both ears were infected. He put Luke on a round of antibiotics and assured me that Luke would be fine within a week.

Luke's screaming and crying worsened, if that was even possible. I took him back to the doctor a week later and got him to look at Luke's ears again.

The antibiotics hadn't touched the infection in Luke's ears. The doctor scratched his head, shrugged, then switched to another antibiotic, claiming that this antibiotic was the most powerful one on the market, and would do the trick.

But that antibiotic didn't work, either. The doctor switched to another antibiotic, and then to another, all to no avail. Nothing was able to touch the raging infection in Luke's ears.

The diarrhea started just after the endless rounds of antibiotics began. Then shortly after that, a thick, white substance coated Luke's tongue. I pointed it out to the doctor and he declared it to be thrush; a yeast overgrowth, he said, and nothing to worry about.

The months dragged on and the seasons changed.

Luke started to walk at around the age of one, but he walked high up on his toes instead of the usual pitter-patter toddlers did. He also would lie on the floor and line up toys until they were in a precise row, flapping his hands in delight when he got them just the way he wanted.

When the words should have come, he remained mute, except for echolalia, or the repetition of words or noises, which, in his case, were noises, since he was completely non-verbal. He would rock back and forth while humming for hours at a time, sounding like a symphony of cicadas on a warm summer night.

It was enough to drive a sane person mad.

By the age of two, Luke's hyperactivity had increased so much that he had become a whirling dervish of energy; racing into walls, bouncing off them, then turning around and running into the opposite wall. He mastered the art of unlocking doors. There was many a day I would look out my front window and see him running down the street as if he was sprinting toward the finish line of a local race. I would have to bolt out the door, chase him down, and drag him back into the house, screaming at him as fear wracked my body.

I would fall into bed each night, exhausted and scared, fearful of what the rising sun would bring.

One drizzling spring day, I carried Luke into the doctor's office, my arms stretched around my child in a vise-like grip. He had clutched in his hand a wooden Thomas the Tank Engine that he took with him everywhere. He wriggled out of my arms as I plopped into a chair, then stretched out on the tile floor, pushing his train back and forth on an imaginary track.

I pushed a strand of damp hair from my eye and stifled a groan. The doctor looked up from his chart and cringed when he saw me. "Yikes! You look like something the cat dragged in. What's wrong? What's wrong?"

By now I was used to the doctor's eccentric sense of humor and smiled despite myself. "You try keeping up with a bundle of energy like this," pointing at Luke, "and see if you look any better."

He peered at the messy bun sitting on top of my head, moved his gaze downward until he was looking at the black tent dress I was wearing, then clucked his tongue. "You need to take better care of yourself. You look like you've gained twenty pounds, and you have bags under your eyes. And, for the love of God, would it hurt you to put on a little make-up?"

"Thanks, *friend*," I said with a sigh. "But Luke is wearing me out too much to take care of myself. Gary has gotten to where he stays at the office every night, so he's no help."

"Use some of your husband's money and hire yourself a babysitter," the doctor suggested. "Or put your son in daycare and give yourself a break."

"Gary never wanted me to put Luke in daycare, so I've been taking him to the office with me. But lately it's been more about me chasing after him than getting any work done."

I paused for a moment as a thought popped into my head. "But he never said anything about a babysitter." I beamed as I looked up at the doctor. "A babysitter is a great idea! That's just what we need. Though I can't imagine what poor soul would put up with us. Luke is non-stop, and we *still* can't get his ears cleared up."

The doctor ran a hand through his mop of black curls and frowned. "We've been through every antibiotic there is. It's time to send him to a specialist and see about getting some tubes put in his ears."

I jumped up and grabbed Luke just as he was about to climb onto the doctor's desk, then pulled him onto my lap. "I think it's allergies causing his ear infections. Maybe we should see an allergist instead."

The doctor bolted upright in his chair and shook his head so hard I thought he was going to give himself a concussion. "Madam, allergies do *not* cause ear infections!" he bellowed.

"How do you know that?" I asked.

"Because allergies can't be measured," he sniffed.

"We have to do something different, because the antibiotics aren't working, and I can't keep going on like this," I cried. "Besides, he's almost three years old, and he still hasn't said a word. Not one peep. Something's wrong, and we have to figure out what it is."

The doctor reached for his phone, dialed a number, then held a hand over the receiver and mumbled, "I'm making him an appointment with an ear specialist to get tubes put in his ears. That'll take care of it for sure."

I folded my arms and tilted my head at him. "You keep saying that, but so far *nothing* has taken care of it."

The doctor flashed me a smile. "This time it will for sure. Trust me. I'm a doctor."

Chapter 3

Luke turned three years old, and still didn't talk. At all. Not even a "mommy" or a "daddy" escaped his lips. I took him to the specialist his pediatrician had recommended. The doctor, a genial man with a quick laugh, placed tubes in both of Luke's ears. He explained to me that the tubes would drain Luke's ears of fluid, and then he would be able to hear better, and thus, start talking.

Luke had his hearing tested shortly after the tubes were placed in his ears, and the doctor said his hearing was normal. "He should start talking any day now!" the doctor cried, and gave me a reassuring pat on the back.

I waited with bated breath for Luke to say his first word, longing to hear "mama" whispered to me in his childish voice. But my son remained mute.

And, oh, so hyper.

I had to carry him everywhere. If I put him down for one second, he'd be off and running, and then I would be chasing him down, puffing and panting, looking like a fool.

One day we were in downtown Atlanta at a conference with Gary. I was going to take Luke across the street to see the *Lion King* at the Fox theatre while Gary was in his class, since we had received free tickets from the conference organizers. I turned my back on Luke for one second to kiss Gary goodbye, and when I turned back around, Luke was gone. My heart pounded and sweat coated my body as I darted from room to room, screaming Luke's name. Somehow, I had the presence of mind to look out the front window of the building. Sure enough, there Luke was; standing on the other side of the street in front of the famed theatre, waving at me, a devilish grin plastered across his face.

My three-year-old son had crossed Peachtree Street by himself; the same street that the famed author Margaret Mitchell, a grown woman, was crossing when she got hit by a car and died. The kid had *no fear*. It was almost as if he had a guardian angel sitting on his shoulder. (In my mind, his twin watched over him, which gave me great comfort.)

But just to be on the safe side, I bought one of those leashes that were made for kids and tied one end of it around Luke's wrist and the other end around mine. I received horrified looks by passersby as we walked down the street, and the occasional snarky comment about treating my son like a dog. I ignored them all, knowing that at least Luke couldn't dart out in front of traffic, or run off and be snatched by a stranger.

My family frowned upon my perceived lack of parental skills when I would bring Luke to family events, and I heard "bad mom" whispered behind hands a time or two. I would place him in one of those high chairs on rollers when we would meet at a restaurant, but somehow he managed to wheel himself across the crowded room, shouting with glee as he waved his arms, dodging stunned diners. All eyes would be upon us as I would scurry across the room and lunge at the runaway high chair with my errant son in it. My mom would cluck her tongue at me, and my sister-in-law would roll her eyes and shake her head, while Luke's cousins guffawed, drawing even more stares.

But I was too beaten down by life to worry about what my family or anyone else, for that matter, had to say about me or Luke.

It was around this time that the word *autism* swirled around our heads, mostly from teachers at Luke's Sunday School class. I poo-pooed the idea, since they had taught us in nursing school, what little had been said about the disorder, was the classic Kanner's autism. The findings of Leo Kanner, an Austrian-born American child psychiatrist (1896-1981), described a group of children as having a lack of attachment, avoidance of eye contact, lack of social interaction, resistance to change, exhibiting repetitive actions, as well as intellectual retardation and a language disorder.[1] We learned that people who had autism weren't able to care for themselves and usually ended up in an institution.

In my mind, Luke's symptoms weren't severe enough to warrant an autism label.

But I knew something was wrong with Luke. I couldn't ignore the ominous symptoms that he displayed any longer. It was time to find answers. Since his hearing was "normal," the only recourse would be to take him to a developmental psychologist.

So, one bleak winter's day I bundled Luke up and drove him to the Marcus Center in Atlanta, an organization that diagnoses and treats autism. My husband Gary came with us, which I was oh so grateful for his support.

A team of two doctors, a child psychologist and a speech therapist were very kind and professional. They made Gary and I as comfortable as we could get, then went about evaluating Luke. Four hours later they sat my husband and I down and formed a circle around us.

The lead doctor, a woman in her mid-forties who specialized in developmental disorders, broke the silence that hung over us like a heavy pall. "I'm sorry to tell you this, but Luke is autistic," she said in a gentle voice. "He's straddling the fence, so to speak, so we're giving him a label of PDD, or Pervasive Developmental Disorder, which is a milder form of the disorder. Luke's autism is actually the mildest of the mild."

I felt the room start to spin as my nursing instructor's words rushed into my head … *Autistic people are profoundly disabled … institutionalized … unable to care for themselves. There is no hope for their future. No cure.* A feeling of dread flooded the pit of my stomach, making me queasy. My mouth hung open like a flopping fish as I floundered to find words. "But, but, but …"

The doctor silenced me with her hand, her eyes flashing me a sympathetic look. "His nonverbal IQ is quite high," she continued. "But his verbal IQ is low, and drops his total score to 101, which is within average intelligence range."

The speech therapist nodded and spoke up. "Luke falls behind his age group in both receptive and expressive language. He has trouble staying on task, and resists change."

The developmental psychologist added her own perceptions. "Luke is a sweet child, but he fails to meet the milestones of his typically-developing peers."

The other doctor, the lone male on the team, a thirty-something guy with long, brown curls and wearing thick glasses, spoke for the first time. "So, we're all in agreement that Luke is on the autism spectrum." He looked around the group, as if seeking validation, and received nods of agreement from the other specialists.

Each damning statement felt like a nail in my son's coffin. I jumped out of the chair I was occupying, my arms flailing and my eyes wild. "My son is *not* autistic!" I cried. "You're all wrong!"

Gary put a restraining hand on my arm and pulled me back into my seat. "There, there, now," he said, patting my hand. "We'll get Luke the help he needs. Even if it means me selling my practice and us moving to another town. Whatever it takes."

Somewhat mollified by my husband's soothing words, I asked in a more subdued voice, "How can you call it autism when you know that Luke had a twin who wasn't fully developed, and died? Wouldn't you think it's something medical? Especially when it's that mild. 'Straddling the fence,' you said. If it's so mild, then why can't it be something else? Something treatable?"

The doctor held out her hands and shrugged her shoulders, her chocolate eyes swimming with compassion. "We don't know what else to call it," she said with a mournful shake of her head. "And there is no cure for autism. It's a disorder, *not* a disease."

I leaned forward in my chair and gripped the arms. "By golly, I *will* find out what to call it!" I vowed. "I don't care how long it takes, or how much it costs me. I'll go to the end of the Earth if I have to. I'll spend every last dime I have until I'm dead-broke. But I promise you right here and now, I'll find out what's *really* wrong with my son."

Thus began my embarkment into no-man's land, into the mysterious world of autism, where no one seems to really know the cause of this heart-breaking disorder.

Chapter 4

Since the small town that we lived in didn't have the resources to deal with an autistic child, I searched several states for a school that could accommodate Luke's special needs. Knowing that Gary would 'sell everything and go with us' gave me the strength I needed in such a stressful time in our lives.

I settled on a school in Nashville, Tennessee, called High Hopes. I felt a sense of acceptance and belonging as soon as I walked through the front door of the small school, and everyone went out of their way to make Luke and I feel welcome.

After I enrolled Luke in their program, I rushed back to our farm and cooked Gary's favorite dinner. I then paced the floor as I waited for him to get home, so anxious to tell him the good news, and so excited about starting our new lives together in Nashville.

As soon as Gary got home, I ushered him to the dining room table and set his plate in front of him with a flourish. I plunked into the chair beside him, gushing about the new school.

"You and Luke will be very happy there," Gary said as he bit into a chicken leg.

I grasped Gary's arm and stared into his cold, impassive eyes. "*We* will be very happy there. As a family. It has mountains and fishing and cozy log cabins ... everything you love!"

Gary drained his glass of tea and smacked his lips, then stabbed a biscuit. "I can't leave. I have a practice to run."

I felt my chin quiver as tears slipped down my face. "But you promised. I can't do this by myself." I swallowed a lump and whispered, "I'm scared."

Gary wiped his mouth, pulled his chair back, then drew me into his arms and murmured into my hair, "Baby, someone has to pay for all of this." He kissed the top of my head. "Now, be strong for Daddy, like a good girl."

I sniffled, nodded once and proceeded to our room to pack, being the dutiful wife that I was.

Luke and I got an apartment near the school, living there during the week, then making the two-hour trek home on the weekends.

I took this time to potty-train Luke. I had read somewhere that the average age of a child with autism became potty-trained was at the age of four. I was determined that Luke would be potty-trained while he was still three. We developed a routine, which is so important for kids on the autism spectrum, as well as to people like myself. Every morning when we would wake up, I would place Luke on his little potty.

The first time we did this I told Luke that we would sit there until he pee-peed in the commode. I sat on the floor beside him and read him stories, the sound of the minute hand ticking away in the background. Fifteen minutes elapsed. Then thirty minutes. Finally, after forty-five minutes of sitting there, I heard a tinkling sound. I jumped up and swooped Luke into my arms, hooting and hollering, and smothered him in kisses.

We did this every morning, never fail. Forty-five minutes dropped to thirty minutes. Then fifteen minutes. The day that Luke climbed out of bed and ran to the potty and pee-peed in it was one of the greatest accomplishments of our lives thus far. I made a huge fuss over him and he beamed at me.

We did pretty much the same routine for pooping in the potty. I had read that one could train their bowels by establishing a time that works around their schedule. For us, the best time to train Luke's bowels was just after breakfast, since eating stimulates peristalsis, an involuntary muscle contraction that moves food down the GI tract. Though he still had diarrhea, our goal was to get Luke to control his bowels until he could go in the potty.

Luke sat on his little potty every morning after he ate his breakfast. I advised him not to strain to push the poop out of his body, but to sit naturally and try to relax. Once again, we read books and sang songs to pass the time. After about five days of following a strict schedule of eating breakfast then sitting on the commode, Luke pooped into the potty for the first time in his life. I showed him how to clean himself and to wash his hands afterwards, then rewarded him with extra hugs and kisses.

With this strict regimen, it had taken just a week to fully potty-train Luke.

Potty-training is such a major hurdle to clear for special needs kids, as well as an advancement towards a life of independence, which is what many of us desperately strive towards. And, the sooner that we can start on this major task, the easier it should be to attain.

The school had an amazing staff who were very supportive of what I was doing with Luke, and never gave me a hard time when I dragged him into school an hour late. The receptionist was a wonderful woman who always had time to listen to me when I needed someone to talk to, and the speech therapists and behavioral specialists were top-notch, as well as an amazing occupational therapist, whom I credit with putting Luke on the road to recovery.

We had been at the school about a month when Sarah, his occupational therapist, a timid girl in her twenties with a gentle smile, commented that Luke tugged at his ears a lot. She also said that he sniffled and sneezed throughout the day, and that he had a runny nose most days. I explained to her that he was under a doctor's care for chronic ear infections, and that the doctor had him on continuous antibiotics.

"Have you ever had Luke tested for allergies?" Sarah asked me.

"His pediatrician doesn't believe in allergies," I replied. "He said that if they can't be measured then they aren't real."

"There's an allergy doctor in Towson, Maryland who specializes in children with autism. His name is Dr. Richard Layton." Sarah glanced over at Luke, who was lying on the floor, staring at wooden trains that he had lined up in a row, oblivious to the bevy of activity around him. "I really think Luke doesn't hear very well," she added.

"Well, the doctors placed tubes in his ears and said his hearing is normal," I said.

"It won't hurt to go see Dr. Layton," Sarah replied.

I took Luke home and looked up Dr. Layton on the internet. I called his office, was happy with what I was told, and made our appointment and bought our plane tickets.

That weekend, I rushed home and gave Gary the great news about Dr. Layton. Gary gave me a hard time about taking his son to see "every snake oil salesman out there," and we fought long into the night.

"Allergies don't cause ear infections!" Gary bellowed for the umpteenth time. "How many times do I have to repeat myself before it gets through that thick skull of yours?"

"How do you know that?" I cried.

"If it can't be measured then it isn't real," he retorted.

"Hmph," I snorted. "You sound just like the pediatrician now. Must be something they taught you in medical school. Well maybe it's time to try alternative ways for Luke. Obviously, traditional medicine isn't helping him one bit. I listened to his pediatrician for years, and he's had Luke on every antibiotic under the sun, which has done *jack squat* for him."

My voice became muffled as I choked on a sob. "I should have listened to my gut years ago and taken Luke to see an allergist, instead of hanging onto every word of one doctor. Doctors don't know everything, you know. Sometimes it's just an educated guess."

Gary threw up his hands and said in a weary voice, "Do what you want; you always do, anyway."

So, off to Baltimore Luke and I went.

Dr. Layton, a kind man with wavy white hair and a twinkle in his eyes, examined Luke's ears and proclaimed that they were full of fluid. "He hasn't been able to hear a word you say," he said. "The sound waves bounce off the fluid in his ears."

"But the doctors said his hearing is normal," I said.

"That's because they had just placed the tubes in his ears, and the tubes were still patent. His tubes are completely clogged now. I'm going to start him on some allergy drops, and that should clear the fluid so that he can start hearing."

Hope surged inside of me, making me giddy with anticipation. "Do you really think he'll start talking then?" I asked in a breathy voice.

"Give it six weeks," the doctor advised, "then I think he'll start saying his first words."

I clutched Luke to my chest and skipped out of the doctor's office on a cloud of dreams.

Lo and behold. ... the doctor's words rang true. Within six weeks Luke said, "Mama."

It was the happiest day of my life!

The day Luke said, "Daddy," my husband broke into a rare smile. "I'll never doubt you again!" he cried. "Do whatever you need to do."

Within two months of seeing Dr. Layton and starting on the allergy drops, the words were flowing from Luke's mouth, which I was thrilled with. By this time, he was fully potty-trained, he was doing well in his classes and he was calm and happy.

Life was finally good!

After six months at the special needs school, the staff pronounced Luke ready for mainstream preschool, marveling about his intelligence. His emerging language skills revealed a genius mind, his teachers would gush. Since he had started talking, he would name all of the state capitols, calculate math problems in his head, draw a picture just from looking at it once and recall the date and year of any event in his life.

I didn't realize it at the time, but these were actually splinter skills related to savant syndrome, or "islands of genius." One in ten individuals with autism display some form of savant syndrome, which always involves tremendous memory, whether it be in music, math, art, calendar-calculating or maps and directions. It is thought that fifty percent of people with savant syndrome are on the autism spectrum, while the other fifty percent have some form of central nervous system injury or disease. There is no known cause of savant syndrome, and it's thought that the skills are not diminished during the savant's lifetime.[2]

Luke and I left his special needs school amidst a flurry of tears and good wishes. I was certain that Luke was on the road to recovery. I took my son back home to our farm and enrolled him in our local preschool.

After about a week of being back home on our farm, Luke's old behavioral issues came roaring back. His screams would echo down the hall as he threw tantrums that would appear out of nowhere, and he would race around the house bouncing off the walls until he dropped from exhaustion.

My stress level skyrocketed until I was a bundle of jangling nerves. But I had no one to turn to, no close friends to talk to, no respite. Gary had come home after we returned from Nashville but turned tail and beat a hasty retreat back to the office after the first tantrum, and my so-called "friends" abandoned me right after Luke was diagnosed as being autistic. So, I was barely holding myself together throughout this emotional storm, knowing I had to be strong for Luke.

For Luke's fourth birthday, I arranged a party for him at the Chuck E. Cheese's, a pizza place that has kids' games to play. My family drove over from South Carolina for the occasion. Gary, though, was noticeably absent, with the excuse that he was too busy saving lives to join us.

Our reserved table was adorned with colorful balloons, streamers, and a gigantic cake with Thomas the Tank Engine as the centerpiece. We had just been seated when Luke's eyes lit up like firecrackers on the Fourth of July.

Forget about the balloons and the cake.

I glanced over to see what had caught Luke's attention. In that moment's hesitation, he was off like a shot, buoyed on by his cheering cousins.

I took off after him, huffing and puffing, dreading where he might be going. But I was way too slow for him.

Luke raced across the room, weaving in and out of tables full of people, and reached the object of his fascination ... a bright red, shiny, fire alarm. He turned to give me a devilish grin, then yanked it down with one swoop. A shrieking noise pierced the air and lights flashed!

I grabbed my deviant child and dragged him, squirming and kicking to get out of my grasp, past our table and towards the nearest exit. I saw out of the corner of my eye my mom watching the drama unfold with her arms crossed and her lips pursed. My sister-in-law turned her back to us as if she didn't know us, while the cousins fell out of their chairs laughing.

Meanwhile, from the back of the room some wise-guy yelled, "Learn how to control your child!" to our retreating backs.

Amidst all the bedlam a long-legged, lithe teen-aged girl with hair the color of honey, approached us as we were leaving the restaurant. She smiled, placed a hand with chipped neon green nail polish on Luke's arm and said in a soft, country twang, "Here, let me help."

Luke tore out of my grip and ran into her outstretched arms as if entranced by her turquoise eyes.

She tickled Luke then looked up at me. "You're Dr. South's wife, ain't you? He takes care of my grandma. I seen you and your son around town."

I wiped away the tears of humiliation that had prickled my eyes and nodded. I then glanced over as a skinny guy in his mid-twenties scurried towards us, his face scrunched in a scowl, just as two fire engines pulled up in front of the restaurant with sirens blaring.

"I think it's time to go before we get hauled off in a police cruiser," I muttered.

The girl looked at the guy and smirked. "Oh, that's just Fred, the assistant manager. I'll take care of him."

She tossed her mane and sashayed up to the guy, Luke following her as if she were the Pied Piper himself. She squeezed the guy's arm, then bent over and whispered in his ear. He glared at Luke, then nodded, turned around and walked importantly out the front door towards the firemen.

"Everything's taken care of," she said. "Fred said you can stay for your party."

"Wow, you sure have a way with guys," I exclaimed, looking over at Luke snuggled in her arms. "Do you know my husband?"

"*Everyone* knows your husband," the girl replied. "He's a rock star."

I gave her a puzzled look. "Are you sure we're talking about the same guy? My husband is *no* rock star."

"Dr. South is dreamy," the girl sighed, then tickled Luke again, making him break out in peals of laughter. "Now, let's get back to your party. I'll stay with Luke. As a matter of fact, I would love to babysit Luke any time you need a break."

I perked up at that thought, feeling like a dog that had just been thrown a bone. "Well, I *have* been trying to find Luke a babysitter. It just never happened, since I was never able to find anyone brave enough to take on the challenge." I cocked my head at her and said with a laugh, "And you know Luke's name. That's pretty impressive."

The girl gave me a sunny smile, revealing white, even teeth. "I know *everything* about you. *I'm* your babysitter now. Any time you need me." She paused for a second, then added, "Or when Dr. South needs me."

The red flags couldn't have been more obvious if they had beaten me over the head, though I was too blind to see them.

After the party fiasco, I called Dr. Layton and asked him to call in a prescription for Ritalin, a drug used to treat ADHD or attention deficit hyperactivity disorder, to our local pharmacy. He was hesitant to at first due to Luke's tender age, but I pleaded with him. I told him that I was losing my mind, and that my husband had stopped coming home because he couldn't handle the stress. The doctor acquiesced and started Luke on a low dose.

The Ritalin stopped Luke in his tracks. But his hyperactivity was replaced with crying spells. He would start crying as soon as he woke up in the morning, continuing along the way to school, and did not stop until he fell asleep at night. I would hold him and rock him, telling him that he would be okay, to no avail.

After about a week of this, Luke woke up one morning, looked me square in the eye and said, "I'm depressed." I sent him off to school and called Dr. Layton.

"How can a four-year-old know about depression?" I cried into the phone.

"Luke is no ordinary four-year-old," Dr. Layton replied. "He's smarter than *all* of us."

The doctor stopped the Ritalin and started Luke on Adderall, another drug used to treat ADHD.

The crying stopped, replaced with an eerie calm. A week later, Luke came up to me, placed his hand in mine, and said, "I want to kill myself."

I grabbed the prescription bottle and flushed the pills down the commode, my body trembling as I battled to control the panic that swept over my body like a raging tsunami. *No more drugs*, I vowed to myself. *I don't care how bad things get. I'm not drugging my son again.*

I took Luke off of the Adderall and decided to tough it out. I didn't take Luke to see Dr. Layton again after the ADHD medication disaster, but not for that reason. I felt that we had run our course with him and the allergy drops that had been so crucial in Luke's speech development, were not beneficial in regulating his behavioral outbursts.

Dr. Layton was a wonderful doctor, and I credit him with enabling Luke's speech.

Disclaimer: I have since found out that Dr. Layton, along with a long list of other doctors who practiced medicine along the guidelines of the DAN! (Defeat Autism Now!) protocol, have been reprimanded and fined for "failing to meet appropriate standards of care."[3] One of the allegations against Dr. Layton was that he was administering low dose allergen therapy (LDA) which is "not approved by the FDA for the treatment of allergies or ASD," (Autism spectrum disorder). Dr. Layton treated Luke's chronic ear infections with LDA, thus stopping his ear infections, which had not responded to continuous antibiotic therapy. Dr. Layton's LDA treatment enabled Luke's speech, with no discernible side effects noted.

DAN! was founded in 1995 by Dr. Bernard Rimland, considered to be the modern-day father of autism. It was he who debunked the theory that autism is caused by "refrigerator" moms. The DAN! protocol consisted of biomedical treatments, theorizing that autism was caused by impaired immune system, external toxins such as mercury from vaccines and the environment, and food sensitivities. Doctors were trained at seminars how to treat kids with autism using the DAN! protocol, and thus were considered to be DAN! doctors. DAN! had many critics, some who scoffed at the idea that autism could be "cured." Others still, took offense to the term "defeat autism," when they accepted the autistic person in their life for the unique individual that they were. The DAN! protocol was shut down in 2011.[4]

In hindsight, I'm forever thankful for the DAN! protocol. It may not have "cured" Luke from autism, but it had lessened his symptoms to the point that he was no longer considered autistic, and was able to live an independent, happy life as a productive member of society. The traits may always be there, lurking in the background, unless he somehow outgrows them ... who knows, with this mysterious disorder? But with diet and supplementation, Luke leads a normal life, which is what any parent could wish for their child.

I have learned in life that there will always be naysayers. Especially when it comes to the subject of autism. I have come to the realization that there appear to be different subsets of autism, so what treatment works for one autistic individual may not work for another. The key is to keep an open mind, and to try a new treatment in a safe environment. LDA was very safe for Luke. He had no adverse reactions to the treatment, and it stopped his ear infections, which paved the way for the development of his speech. I give all the credit to Dr. Layton for this; I'll never forget him and will sing his praises into eternity.

It was during all the commotion with the medication that I tried to teach Luke how to ride the bicycle that I had given him for his birthday. Every day after school, I would put Luke on his shiny new bike and push him down the grassy knoll behind our house, then let go and jog by his side as he wobbled down the path. Even with training wheels attached to the bicycle, he managed to tip over in the lush grass. I would pick him up, dust him off and put him back on the bike, telling him that he would master the art of riding a bicycle in no time. I would then give the bike a big heave and push Luke down the path again, with him fussing and whimpering the whole way. He would proceed to splat onto the ground, then clutch his leg and howl as if it had just been mangled.

After about a week of this, I walked into the garage and noticed that Luke's bicycle was missing. I turned to him and asked in a puzzled voice, "Where's your bicycle?"

Luke glanced over at the muddy hole where our pool was being built and shrugged his shoulders. He then turned on his heel and fled into the house.

A month later, one of the workers knocked on our door and presented me with a mud-encrusted bicycle. "Looky what I found when I drained the dirty water from your pool," he said. "Looks like someone didn't want to learn how to ride his bike," he added with a chuckle.

That ended our bike-riding endeavor. Luke appeared to lack the coordination to stay upright on the bicycle, and the frustration he displayed made the experience too unpleasant to continue.

I also noted the uncoordinated way he ran, his arms flopping at his side and his unbalanced gait. He appeared to have fine motor skills deficits, as well. I tried to teach him how to tie his shoes until we both screamed in frustration, but his fingers were too clumsy to tie the laces. I had to end up buying him shoes made with Velcro flaps.

We experienced highs and lows for the next several months, albeit more lows than highs. But at least Luke wasn't talking about suicide anymore, and the crying had stopped for good.

Meanwhile, the babysitter had ensconced herself in our lives. She stayed with Luke while I went to the gym that had just opened in our town. She also took him to the park, so I could have "me time," which was wonderful, I have to admit, like a gift from the gods. Luke adored her, and was on his best behavior when he was around her. He clung to her like she was a lifeline.

Soon after the babysitter entered our lives, the rumors began to swirl that she was having an affair with Gary. I would see women whispering behind their hands in the check-out line at the grocery store, then give me a sidelong glance, and a chill would creep up my spine. But I rationalized that the girl was a teenager, and surely Gary wasn't stupid enough to risk his marriage, as well as his reputation, for a fling with a young girl.

I defended the babysitter to anyone who had the audacity to say anything to me about her. She came into our lives after Gary had checked himself out of the family life, and nurtured Luke with the love and acceptance he so desperately needed.

So, I stuck my head in the sand and carried on with our lives. That lasted until the day Gary moved out of our house for good and into the upstairs apartment of his office. His rationale was that he needed peace and quiet in his life, which he was unable to get in his own home, thanks to Luke's shenanigans.

After Gary officially moved out, the babysitter couldn't ditch Luke and I fast enough. How the tongues wagged that Gary had traded me in for the babysitter, and was just using Luke as an excuse to abandon his family for greener pastures.

I picked up the shattered pieces of our lives, my mind numb with grief. Yet another person had exited Luke's life when he was the most vulnerable. How my heart broke for him. But I (foolishly) held out hope that Gary would come to his senses when he realized how much his son needed him, and come home.

The days passed in a blur ... Luke and I against the world, with no Gary in sight, save the rare obligatory appearance. And, no more babysitters, since the last one ended up stealing my husband.

My new gym membership was the first thing to go by the wayside. My weight mushroomed, and I felt the depression swallow me into a dark abyss.

Luke's behavioral issues escalated with every approaching birthday. The principal of his school must have had my number on speed-dial, as much as she called me into her office for Luke's latest provocation.

One frigid winter's day when Luke was seven, we pulled up in our yard, my mind reeling from yet *another* confrontation with Luke's principal over his bad behavior. I stared at the old well as I turned off the ignition.

Just then, I jolted upright as a thought pushed its way through the fog that had clouded my head. I felt as if someone had flipped a switch in my brain and illuminated a path for me. My jaw dropped as I turned and gaped at Luke fiddling with his Gameboy.

I realized then what was wrong with Luke, as well as what had killed his twin!

Chapter 5

All the years of anguishing over what was wrong with Luke and what had killed his twin...*what had I done wrong? Was it something I ate? Something I drank?* ... and the answer had been right before my eyes all this time. I had been just too blind to see it.

I needed proof that my theory was correct, though. I scourged the internet for environmental doctors and was delighted to find one not too far away from where we lived. I made an appointment with the doctor, giddy with hope.

Two weeks later, I bundled Luke up, and we made the hour-long trek to Atlanta. Snow flurries pelted the car as we turned into a medical plaza perched along the perimeter of the sprawling metropolis.

Luke hadn't put both feet through the doorway of the doctor's office when the doctor, a white-haired, bespectacled man with a bald pate that gleamed in the artificial light, looked up from the chart he had been studying. He took one look at my son then bellowed, "He's not autistic. He's *toxic!*"

My heart pounded as visions of a healthy, *normal* child danced through my head. I sank into a leather Queen Anne chair that faced the doctor's massive mahogany desk and asked in a breathless whisper, "Do you really think so?"

"I *know* so," the doctor replied. "Look at how he carries his body. The way he walks high up on his toes. His low muscle tone. His lack of coordination. The dull look in his eyes."

He came around his desk, resplendent in a crisp white lab coat and red tie, looking every inch the professional. He grasped Luke by his chin, then peered inside Luke's mouth and grunted. "Just what I thought. His tongue is coated with thrush, which means he has a yeast overgrowth; which means he most likely has leaky gut."

"But his pediatrician said yeast is harmless!" I cried. "And, what the heck is *leaky* gut?"

"Leaky gut is a condition in which the small intestine is damaged, and undigested food particles and toxins leak through the lining and are dumped into the blood stream. The immune system then attacks them like they are a foreign body, which causes inflammation, and can cause food sensitivities."

The doctor leaned against the edge of his desk and tapped the chart he had been reading. "Your son has had massive amounts of antibiotics over the years, which destroy the good bacteria in the gut, causing dysbiosis, which causes an overgrowth of yeast. This, in turn, breaks down the lining of the intestine. I'm afraid we're also going to find malabsorption, which would explain his chronic diarrhea."

"Why didn't his pediatrician tell me about this leaky gut?" I asked. "We could have been treating it all these years."

"That's because traditional doctors aren't taught in medical school about leaky gut. It's a gray area … like allergies causing ear infections. They don't believe in it because it can't be measured, so, therefore, it can't be proven. And, if it can't be proven, then it doesn't exist."

He picked up Luke's chart and opened it. "It says here that your husband is a doctor. What does he have to say about all of this?" He glanced up at the door, as if expecting my husband to burst through it at any moment. "By the way, where is he, anyway? Shouldn't he be here for something this important?"

I plucked at a hole that graced the voluminous shirt I was wearing, not daring to meet the doctor's gaze. "I, um, uh. I mean, he's not here," I muttered, stumbling over my words.

I cleared my throat, stole a glance at Luke, who was pacing back and forth, flapping his hands, then said, "He doesn't come home anymore. He said he can't take the chaos in our house; said something about needing peace and quiet."

I stared at my hands and felt my face flush. "He refused to come. Said you were a snake oil salesman," I mumbled.

The doctor threw his head back and laughed. "A *snake oil salesman*? I've been called worse."

He placed his hand on my shoulder and gave it a gentle squeeze. "We'll get you that peace and quiet. You came to the right place." He shifted his gaze toward Luke. "We'll do some testing, just to be sure. But I'm positive we'll find that his body is overloaded with heavy metals."

"But we had a blood test done for heavy metals when he was little," I said shaking my head, "and the test came back negative."

"That's because the heavy metals were already stored in his soft tissues," the doctor said. "Those blood tests only show positive results for *acute* heavy metal poisoning, which means that they were ingested very recently."

He scribbled something in Luke's chart, snapped his pen shut, then looked up at me. "Let's get started, shall we?"

The doctor did a heavy metal challenge, where he administered DMSA, which is a chelator that pulls the heavy metals from soft tissues, such as bone marrow, kidneys, the lungs and the brain. He also did a urine test to look for leaky gut, a stool test to detect malabsorption, and drew blood to determine electrolyte levels as well as a complete blood count.

He then did a SPECT scan on Luke, or single photon emission computerized tomography, which is a brain scan. The doctor explained that the SPECT scan can detect heavy metals by pinpointing areas of the brain which have either reduced or increased blood flow, which can signify a disease process.

The doctor called a few weeks later and crowed into the phone, "I knew it! Your son has heavy metal poisoning; his body is full of lead, aluminum, arsenic and mercury, as well as pesticides. His levels are off the charts. The SPECT scan showed that his brain is full of heavy metals. His brain is functioning at a seventy-eight IQ level."

The doctor paused for a second, then said in a gentle voice, "And *that*, my dear lady, is what killed his twin. Luke got enough heavy metals to damage his body, but his twin got the brunt of it … enough to kill him."

A sick feeling flooded the pit of my stomach as I realized my theory was correct, and what had caused it.

"How did it get there?" I asked, my hand trembling as it gripped the phone, dreading the answer, but already knowing it.

"From you … and your well," the doctor replied. "Your well water is contaminated. Back in the old days the farmers used pesticides, which were full of arsenic and mercury, on their crops. They stored them in barns, like the one you said you have next to your well. Over the years the poison seeped into the ground and got into your water."

I gasped for air, as if I had just been punched in the solar plexus. "Bu...bu...but we had the water tested when we moved into the house!"

"Get them to test it again," the doctor advised. "Make sure you specify testing for heavy metals. Oh, and by the way, the lead came from the paint you scraped off the walls. Lead dust is invisible. You didn't even realize you were inhaling it. So, most likely, you're full of heavy metals too, and need to get treated, along with your son."

"I would advise you to think twice about allowing your son to get anymore vaccines," he continued. "Your son can't take anymore insult to his already overburdened body. Vaccines have heavy metals in them."

"I know the vaccines have mercury in them," I said, "but it's supposed to be a minuscule amount. Not enough to do any damage."

A swift "hmphh" greeted my ear. "That's what they *want* you to believe," he muttered, then cleared his throat and plowed ahead, his voice rising an octave. "The vaccine manufacturers have agreed to take Thimerosal, which is a preservative they use to keep the vaccines from going bad, out of the vaccines, since the Thimerosal contains mercury. But even without the Thimerosal, the vaccines still contain mercury, just not as much. Vaccines also have aluminum in them; it's used as an adjuvant, which means it prompts a response from the immune system and helps the vaccine work better. Aluminum is a heavy metal." He cleared his throat.

"They started injecting your son with these toxins when he was struggling to stay alive. His body couldn't take the added burden of these heavy metals. All the mercury and aluminum stored in his brain has caused his speech, attention span, memory and coordination issues, as well as the anxiety you said he has. It's done a lot of damage that, hopefully, we can undo. He's seven years old. We still have a little time left … around three years. His brain should still be elastic enough until around the age of ten to recover from most of the insult."

The doctor took a deep breath, as if coming up for air. "Luke is very lucky to be alive right now, but he needs treatment immediately. He has a lot of damage to his GI tract, as well as his liver. But it's his GI tract that I'm most concerned about right now. He has leaky gut, as well as severe malabsorption. He has *no* amino acids left in his body. He will die if we don't start treatment immediately."

I swallowed a lump in my throat and asked in a shaky voice, "How do you propose to do that?"

"To start with, we need to remove gluten, dairy and sugar from his diet. Those are the main offenders in leaky gut."

"But we had Luke tested for gluten and dairy allergies, and he tested negative," I said.

"Being allergic to something and being sensitive are two different things," the doctor explained. "An allergy triggers the immune system to cause a reaction. A sensitivity is a gut reaction to a food that the digestive system can't break down, so your symptoms are going to be gas and bloating, constipation, behavior issues, nausea, or, in your son's case, diarrhea. Food sensitivities are a major contributor to leaky gut."

"So, my care plan includes removal of gluten, dairy and sugar from his diet, supplement his body with the vitamins and minerals he's deficient in, sauna treatments to remove the pesticides, and DMSA to pull those heavy metals out. Bring your son to my office next week and we'll get started on the DMSA. But I need to warn you: his behavior will get much worse as those metals are coming out. The worse his behavior will be will indicate how much his body is burdened with heavy metals."

I made an appointment to start treatment for Luke, then hung up the phone, my mind awhirl with conflicting emotions. On the one hand, I was relieved the doctor validated my theory as to what had happened to my boys, but on the other hand, I was incensed that he had the audacity to tell me that I was the cause of it. I was a nurse, for God's sake, and my husband a doctor. One would think that between the two of us, one of us should have known better.

I was determined to prove the doctor wrong. The well was the first place to start. I flipped through the phone book until I found the number for the county agent. I called and asked them to come check our water, specifically for heavy metals, and was pleased when they assured me they would be at our farm the next morning.

The agent, a young, slim guy wearing cowboy boots and a denim shirt studded with rhinestones, knelt over the old well and dipped a container in the water. He peered at it, pushed back his cowboy hat adorned with a snake's head, then scratched his head. "Well, ma'am, it looks like you got a ton of arsenic and mercury in your water," he announced in a thick southern twang.

I trembled as I felt anger engulf my body. My fingers balled into fists, wanting so badly to knock that stupid hat off his head. "Why didn't you guys test for heavy metals when you first came out here?" I screamed, "You idiots helped kill my baby!"

"But *no one* has heavy metals in their water," he said with a shrug.

"That's because you idiots never test for it, you imbecile!"

I stormed into the house and slammed the door, already feeling the guilt overwhelm me; guilt for being part of the reason for Luke's disability and his twin's death, and guilt for calling the poor guy an imbecile. I stumbled to the couch and sobbed into a pillow, my mind flooded with depressing thoughts.

My twins got heavy metal poisoning because of me and our farm, and one of them is dead and the other one barely clinging to life, lost in an autistic fugue.

I curled into a tight ball, wanting to stay on the couch until the Grim Reaper came and took me away, to a place of merciful oblivion. But then Luke called for me, and I knew I had a responsibility to him. I wiped my tears, pulled myself off the couch and squared my shoulders.

I may have been part of the problem, but, by golly, I will be very much part of the solution! I thought to myself as I went to check on my son.

Chapter 6

The following week, Luke and I returned to the doctor's office. The doctor came around his desk and hugged me as if we were long, lost friends. He glanced down at the shirt I was wearing, then shifted his gaze towards Luke, who was pacing the floor, high up on his toes.

I felt my face flush as I realized I was wearing the same shirt from our last visit. I fell into a chair and folded my hands in my lap to keep them from fidgeting with the hole in my shirt, which by now was approaching the size of a small crater. I cleared my throat and squeaked, "I um, had our well water tested, and, uh, you were right. It's full of heavy metals."

A smile creased the doctor's face as he eased onto the edge of his desk. "Well, you came to the right place. Let's get started." He pulled a slip of paper from Luke's chart and studied it for a second, then gave it to me. "Here's my proposal to get Luke well."

I plucked the paper from his hand and studied it. "Hmmm … let's see. DMSA therapy. Ok. Vitamins and minerals. Ok …"

My jaw dropped as I pointed to an item on the paper. "$8000 for sauna therapy? That's outrageous!"

"It's for a month's treatment at our facility," the doctor sniffed.

"So that means that I would have to pay for a place to stay for Luke and I for one month," I replied. "I'll have to run that one by my husband. I don't know if he'd like us being gone a whole month."

The doctor raised a bushy eyebrow. "But you said your husband never comes home; so, he wouldn't even know you were gone."

I felt a rosy hue stain my cheeks, and my hand made a beeline for the hole in my shirt, twisting it until my shirt was crumpled like an old rag. "Yeah, well, he might miss us a little … I mean, uh, it could happen," I sputtered, staring at my shoes.

The doctor reached over and touched my shoulder, then gave it a gentle squeeze. "I'm sorry," he said in a soft voice. "Having an autistic child is very hard on a marriage. I've been a doctor a long time, and I've never seen anything like this autism epidemic. Since 1988 the number of kids diagnosed with autism has exploded."

The doctor's voice rose until it echoed off the walls. "Yet some of the so-called "experts" try to tell us that it's just better diagnosing, which is hogwash! But, what they don't tell us is that in 1988 they added a new Hib vaccine, and within the next few years they added four additional vaccines given in the first fifteen months of life. And these vaccines contain mercury and aluminum. That may be ok for your typical child, but for kids with compromised immune systems, or for kids who are genetically pre-disposed, injecting these heavy metals into them overburdens their bodies and they develop autistic tendencies."

The doctor shook his head and continued his ranting, "I don't think that this autism epidemic is classic autism. I think it is heavy metal poisoning, namely mercury and aluminum. Let's look at the symptoms of autism versus the symptoms of mercury poisoning, starting with autism first."

With a dramatic sweep of his hand, the doctor held up five fingers, then closed each finger one by one as he ticked off each symptom. "Social withdrawal. Language deficits. GI problems. Sleep issues. Low muscle tone and incoordination." He took a breath.

"Now let's look at the symptoms of mercury poisoning: speech and hearing impairment. GI problems. Sleep problems. Low muscle tone. Incoordination. Neurological damage. Social withdrawal."

The doctor stopped and pinned me with a probing look. "Do you see what I'm saying?"

"Oh, I totally hear what you're saying," I said. "I always thought that whatever was wrong with Luke was medically-induced, and had everything to do with whatever killed his twin. I'm just happy to finally have answers, and hope to goodness that it's not too late to reverse the damage."

I hung my head and choked on a sob. "Maybe then Gary will want to come home. Not that I should take him back ... the cowardly worm."

The doctor shook his head and sighed. "I've seen first-hand how this autism epidemic has destroyed families. One of the parents, and it's usually the father, isn't strong enough to deal with an autistic child, and abandons the family, leaving the remaining parent, usually the mother, to shoulder the burden of caring for their child alone."

"It hurts," I whispered. "We used to be so happy before we bought that *dang* farm. Then everything went downhill after that: Luke's twin died. Luke became autistic. Gary left us."

I dabbed at a tear that had snaked its way down my face, then found my way back to the hole in my shirt, tugging on it until I heard the material rip. "I feel like I need to divorce him, but I'm scared to be by myself, alone with a special needs child. Besides, I need his money to care for Luke." I hung my head and murmured, "I don't make a salary working in his office, which I do from home now that he left us. I just can't deal with having to look at his cowardly, cheating face every day."

The doctor eased into the chair beside mine and grasped my hand. "Let's focus on getting Luke well, then you can decide what to do about your marriage. But right now, you have a sick child on your hands who will die without medical intervention. We can postpone the sauna therapy for now, but at some point we'll need to start it so we can get those pesticides out. Let's start with the DMSA therapy, and we can start him on his vitamin and mineral therapy concurrently."

He glanced over at Luke, who had parked himself in the doctor's chair and was staring at the monitor while tapping away on the keyboard.

The doctor bolted out of the chair as if he had just sat on a burning ember, shouting, "What the …" He raced around the desk and stood behind Luke.

I jumped up and yelled, "Luke, no! That computer belongs to the doctor!"

The doctor broke into a grin and waved his hands at me. "Sit back down. I actually like what he did." He reached around Luke and swiveled the monitor until it faced me. A picture of the doctor beaming, his arms encircled around a child, flooded the screen. "He made a screensaver of myself and my grandchild. I'm going to keep it like this."

He draped an arm around Luke and said, "This kid is actually very bright. A lot smarter than what the SPECT scan showed. We just need to get those heavy metals out of his brain so that he can lead a relatively normal life. And, to me, the ability to lead an independent life is recovery from autism."

"It's recovery enough for me," I whispered. "It's all I ever wanted for Luke … to grow up to be an independent and free young man, who can stand on his own two feet."

"Well, let's get started then." The doctor reached into a medicine cabinet and pulled out several bottles. "We'll start him on DMSA, which will pull heavy metals out of his soft tissues. He'll also need to take these supplements, since the DMSA also pulls out essential vitamins and minerals. We'll have to keep an eye on his liver and kidney functions to make sure they aren't being stressed by the DMSA, so come back in two weeks and we can test his liver and kidneys, and then we'll start phase two … removing gluten and dairy and sugar from his diet."

He paused as if coming up for air, then added, "Fair warning … I believe I already told you that the DMSA will exacerbate any stereotypical behavior that he ever had as those metals are coming out. The more metals that are in his body, the worse his behavior is going to be. So, batten down your hatches, because the storm is about to hit your home, and it's going to be fierce. You'll be wishing you had the bad behavior that he displays now. But, it should only last for a week or so."

I swallowed hard and made the sign of the cross. "Peace be with us and serenity now." I squared my shoulders and emitted a long, slow sigh, sounding like air whistling out of a deflated balloon. "There, I'm ready for it. Bring it on …"

Chapter 7

Mayhem ruled our house after just one dosage of the DMSA. Every autistic behavior Luke had ever exhibited did become magnified many times over, until he was a whirling dervish of hyperactivity. He would run into the wall, bounce off it, then turn around and run into the other wall. Back and forth, back and forth, he would go, until I became dizzy just watching him; all the while snapping his fingers, flicking his hands and humming in a loud, frenzied tone.

Luke's tantrums were the mother of all tantrums. He would pitch a hissy fit if I didn't give him his way, crying and sniveling for hours, his whining grating on my nerves until I thought I would go mad. But, I managed to keep myself sane by chanting the doctor's words over and over in my mind. *The more metals that are in his body, the worse his behavior is going to be.* I knew that we were on the right track and was prepared with the knowledge that the road to recovery would be a brutal one.

I had forewarned the principal of Luke's school that he was undergoing treatment, and that it would probably be a good idea if I kept him home during that crucial first week. Not that it should have mattered anyway since he was failing all of his classes in the most spectacular fashion. The principal had other ideas. She called one day and informed me that I would be arrested and sent to jail if I kept my child out of school.

So off to school we went.

I marched Luke into the principal's office and deposited him at the front desk. "He's all yours," I said to the startled receptionist. "Don't say I didn't warn you."

I gave Luke a fierce hug, then turned and sauntered off with a defiant flip of my hair.

An hour later the shrilling of my cell phone shattered the blissful quiet. A smirk flitted across my face as I looked at the caller ID. I answered the phone with a bored, "Hello?"

"Hello, Mrs. South? This is Mrs. Black, the principal, calling. We need you to come get your son, Luke. He's a distraction to the rest of the class, and he's been in yet another fight. I swear, if Dr. South hadn't saved my mother's life, your son would have been expelled long ago."

"But, Mrs. Black," I said with exaggerated innocence. "You'll have me locked up if I keep Luke home from school. I think he needs to stay at school, just like you said. You're *so* right. His, ahem, education is *much* more important than my trying to get him better."

The principal gave me a condescending chuckle. "It looks like a little misunderstanding, that's all. You come and get Luke and keep him home as long as you need to, and we'll rescind the warrant for your arrest. He'll be in the front office, waiting for you."

I sugarcoated the sarcasm in my voice with a dollop of the sweetest honey. "Oh, bless your heart, Mrs. Black. You're just so thoughtful. I'll be right there and bring Luke home where he should have been the whole time during this stressful period."

I stepped into the office a few minutes later to see Luke sitting in a chair, a leaf sticking out of his hair, and his shirt muddied and torn. I turned and gave the receptionist a questioning look.

The receptionist picked up the phone as if, all of a sudden, she had an important call to make, shook her head and blew out a long breath.

I scooped Luke up in a bear hug and said in a quiet voice, "Come on, Luke. Let's go home."

Luke got his backpack as I held the door open for him, and we stepped into the hallway, which was packed with kids milling around. A hush descended as Luke muscled his way through the crowd, and a wave of kids parted for Luke as if he were about to walk on water.

We had just reached the front door, when one of the kids, a runty boy with big ears, squinty eyes peeping through thick glasses and freckles covering his face, ran up to me. "Luke's a badass," he gushed. "Chased a bully, who stole his pencil, into the yard and tackled him to the ground." His face glowed as he stared at Luke in awe. "He gives the rest of us kids the courage to stand up to bullies."

At that, all the other kids crowded around Luke, cheering and giving him high fives.

I turned and gaped at my son. "Luke, you beat up a kid?"

Luke replied with a "*hmphh*," held up the pencil in question, and strolled out the door.

After about a week of chaos, the storm began to fizzle out, *thank goodness*, and Luke actually began to calm down. His pacing back and forth and hand flapping stopped as if someone had turned off a faucet, and his anxiety had decreased so much that it became a non-issue. His speech improved dramatically, though he still lagged in conversational skills. He also lost that clumsy gait, though he still walked on his toes.

But, the biggest gain I noticed was that his memory was sharper; he no longer appeared to walk around in a fog. I quit having to remind him every morning to remember to pick his lunch bag off the kitchen counter, and he got to where he didn't have to run around the house trying to remember where he had put his toys.

I have since learned that you can give activated charcoal after giving a dosage of DMSA, and it'll absorb some of the toxins, thus dramatically decreasing the adverse reactions. The charcoal must be given no sooner than two hours after ingesting the DMSA and the supplements, since it absorbs everything in its path … good or bad. So, if you give the activated charcoal less than two hours after the DMSA and the nutrients, the charcoal will absorb them before they have a chance to benefit the body. Also, no more than three capsules of activated charcoal should be given within a twenty-four hour period, or you risk getting constipation.

Now that the DMSA had restored peace and quiet in our house, I turned my attention toward the pesticide poisoning and the sauna therapy. I had recalled that the doctor had said some of the symptoms of pesticide poisoning were the same as mercury poisoning, as well as traits of autism ... poor concentration, or more specifically ADHD, incoordination, muscle weakness and depression.

The doctor had said he would use an infrared sauna. He explained that the infrared light goes several inches under the skin, where the fat deposits are. The pesticides are stored in the fat deposits.

The doctor had quoted a price of $8000 to do sauna therapy for Luke for one month. But I was determined that I could do it myself, at a fraction of the cost.

I just needed to find an infrared sauna.

Being in a small town, there weren't many saunas lying around, especially of the infrared kind. I called our local gym, but they didn't have one. The closest sauna that I could find was in a town almost an hour away.

Disheartened but not discouraged, I turned to the internet for help in finding a sauna. To my delight, I found an infrared sauna with low EMF (Electro-Magnetic Frequency; which means in layman's terms lower radiation) in Canada that was a perfect size for us, and it was around $500. They even shipped it for free. I paid a handyman $100 to put it together, and we were on our way!

I remembered how the doctor had told me how he does his sauna therapy, then did it the exact way he had described it. First of all, we had to take niacin, which is a nutritional supplement found in just about any drug store, and many grocery stores. We had to be sure to get the "flush" niacin, as that causes less stress to the liver. The purpose of the niacin is to cause vasodilation, which means enlarging the blood vessels under the skin, which accounts for the flushing sensation. The vasodilation helps the body to sweat more.

Fair warning ... niacin flush may cause a warm redness of the skin, along with itching and a tingling sensation. It starts about fifteen to twenty minutes after taking the niacin, and it usually lasts about an hour. It's harmless, though may be a bit uncomfortable until you get used to it.

The doctor had explained that the niacin also breaks open the fat cells (lipolysis) which, in turn, mobilizes fat and toxins faster. The toxins are then excreted through the skin via the sweat.

We started off by taking 100mg of the niacin, then bumped it up (titrated) until we were taking 1000mg. A lot of people titrate up to 5000mg, but I found that 1000mg did the trick for us, and Luke tolerated it better.

Thirty minutes after taking the niacin we had to exercise for at least twenty minutes, which raises the body temperature and makes it easier to sweat. So, we ran around the house a few times. We even made a game of it by chasing the chickens around the yard, which ended up being quite fun, and made Luke laugh, which is a beautiful sound, indeed.

After our jog around the yard, we would jump into the sauna, which I would already have pre-heated to 130 degrees

Fahrenheit. At first Luke was only able to tolerate about five minutes of the sauna before he would start fussing and trying to escape. But I put plenty of his favorite books and toys in the sauna and would quiz him on quotes from our favorite movies, which made our time in the sauna much more tolerable. In fact, I have many fond memories of our time in the sauna when the cousins would come visit and we would all pile in and have a merry ole time!

We both built tolerance until we were able to stay in the sauna for an hour, which is the optimal time for detoxifying. After our hour was up, I would have Luke take a shower to rinse off the toxins that may have lingered on his skin.

We did this every day for one month.

After the month was up, I sent off to Doctors Data for a pesticide testing kit, and retested Luke's pesticides level myself. All I had to do was get some urine from Luke and we sent it off. It was simple!

And the test results came back negative for pesticides! So, basically, Luke and I did his sauna therapy ourselves and saved $7400.

It did cost us one doctor, though.

After I got the test results for the pesticides back from the lab, I called the doctor and told him the happy news. He promptly fired me, but not before bellowing in my ear about being a huge liability for him, with no respect for his position … blah, blah, blah.

So, there we were. With no doctor.

Bottom line … I thought this doctor was a bit money-grubbing, but he had the right idea, and he was the one who led Luke down that mystical road to recovery.

Chapter 8

I kept Luke on the DMSA until it ran out about six months later. I would give him two DMSA capsules three times a week for about four weeks, then give his body a break for about eleven weeks, then repeat the process until all of the DMSA was gone. I made sure to give Luke extra vitamins and minerals while he was taking the DMSA, as chelators deplete the body of vital nutrients. I was also able to monitor his liver and kidney functions through our local lab.

Disclaimer ... DMSA should be given *only* under close medical supervision, by a qualified medical professional. DMSA is very effective in removing heavy metals, most notably mercury, cadmium and arsenic, while EDTA is more effective in removing lead.[5] They are not without controversy, though, as chelation has been attributed to three deaths. But after an investigation, it was noted that the deaths occurred secondary to medical errors in giving NAEDTA, which caused hypocalcemia, then death.[6]

Though so many of Luke's autistic traits either subsided or altogether disappeared after going through chelation therapy, I was nervous about the potential side effects of the DMSA; namely, electrolyte imbalance which can lead to dangerous cardiac problems, as well as liver and kidney damage. For this reason, I scoured the internet for a new doctor to treat Luke's heavy metal poisoning.

Through the DAN! website, I found a holistic doctor in Portland, Oregon, whom specialized in chelation therapy. I was fortunate enough to be able to talk to the doctor on the phone before making an appointment. He sounded very knowledgeable about heavy metal removal, as well as a nice guy.

The closest appointment with this DAN! doctor was a month out, so I bided my time researching treatments and supplements.

I stumbled upon milk thistle, which is a flowering plant related to the daisy and the sunflower. Milk thistle is used as an anti-inflammatory as well as an anti-oxidant. It allegedly helps liver cells regenerate after an insult to the liver such as toxins or alcohol.

I knew Luke had liver damage from the heavy metals, so I figured it might help his liver detoxify some of the heavy metal burden. I started him on one capsule a day and monitored him closely.

A day after starting the milk thistle, Luke experienced Herxheimer's reaction, which is the immune system trying to fight off the toxins that have been killed by the milk thistle. Just as with the DMSA, the more severe the reaction, the greater the die-off, which is a very good thing, and means that the milk thistle was working. Symptoms usually include malaise, chills and sweating, nausea and body aches.

A lot of people stop taking the milk thistle after they start experiencing Herxheimer's reaction because it's very uncomfortable. But the key is to stay on it. The symptoms usually go away within three days to a week. Take activated charcoal to reduce the Herxheimer's, but be sure to wait until two hours after ingesting the milk thistle so you won't absorb the benefit of the milk thistle as well.

I started taking the DMSA soon after Luke started on it, since I realized a lot of the toxins he got were from me, and I started the milk thistle the same time he did. The Herxheimer's reaction is very real, and I felt like I wanted to croak for the next three days, barely able to drag myself out of bed. But it passed after three days, and I felt a lot healthier, almost rejuvenated.

Luke and I both continue to take milk thistle to this day, and always will.

Meanwhile, second grade ended and I was informed by Luke's team that he would not be progressing to the third grade with his classmates. They were holding him back in second grade. Their rationale was that he was too far behind the other students academically, as well as in maturity level.

"Let's give him a year to catch up maturity-wise," the principal advised me. "Besides, he's in no hurry to graduate … where else is he going to go?"

I was stunned by the callousness of the comment that the principal had weaseled in. Such a flippant remark was unwarranted, as well as cruel. But, I had to either accept the fact that Luke flunked, or find him another school. At that time, I wasn't ready to uproot him, so I buried the urge to slap the principal, and instead, merely seethed inwardly.

I broke the news to Luke that night over a slice of pepperoni pizza at our favorite pizza place. I bit my lip to keep from squalling as I saw him hang his head mid-bite.

"Why me? What have I done wrong?" he asked through a haze of tears.

I reached across the table and grabbed Luke's hand. "You've done nothing wrong," I cried. "It's just to better prepare you for the years to come. To make your life a little easier."

I lifted Luke's chin and stared into his eyes, my own swimming in tears. "We'll get through this. I promise you, and we'll both be stronger and wiser for this." I managed a feeble smile. "Now let's finish our pizza then we'll skedaddle and go play some putt-putt golf."

One month later, on a cloudless summer day with Mt. Hood soaring on the horizon, Luke and I walked through the door of the doctor's office in Portland. The doctor was tall and muscular, as if he spent his time off in the gym. He had sandy brown hair dusted with silver highlights. The faint lines around the doctor's eyes crinkled as he smiled at Luke, taking my son's hand in his. "How are you, Little Man?"

Luke grunted a "fine" in reply, then ambled toward a table in the corner of the room filled with books and toys. He shuffled a stack of books until he found one that interested him, then plopped into a chair and buried his nose behind the book.

The doctor studied Luke for a minute, then turned to me, a brow arched. "I don't really see anything wrong with him."

I felt my heart flop over in my chest and a smile split open my face as gratitude for this man's compassion flooded my senses. I knew then that we had come to the right place.

"That's the nicest thing anyone's ever said to me!" I gushed.

"I'm serious," the doctor said, easing into a chair beside me. "His eye contact is good and his gross motor skills appear to be within normal limits. He answered me appropriately, albeit, a tad short," he added with a chuckle.

"He's a work-in-progress with his social skills," I said with a laugh.

"Aren't we all," the doctor laughed.

The doctor proceeded to examine Luke, then performed a heavy metal challenge test and drew some blood. After the doctor finished the testing, he turned to me as he washed his hands in the sink. "I really think this kid will outgrow this and live a normal life. Based on his history, I'm confident that we'll find heavy metals in his body, which we'll eradicate with chelators. After we get those metals out, your son should be fine."

I beamed as I arose and clasped the doctor's hand. "Bless you for your kindness," I said, choking back tears. I collected my son, and we walked out of the doctor's office hand in hand, bonded for life in our intense need for each other.

The doctor called a week after we returned home. "The results of the heavy metal challenge showed that there's still a significant burden of heavy metals in Luke's body. Let's start the DMSA again and we'll monitor his progress, as well as keep an eye on his liver and kidney labs. I'm shipping you the DMSA, as well as a good multi-vitamin and several supplements that he'll need."

The doctor paused for a second as if gathering his thoughts, then continued. "I really think we're on the right track here with heavy metals detoxification. In my professional opinion, your son was misdiagnosed with the autism label, especially with the history of his twin's mysterious death. We'll repeat the heavy metal challenge after this round of DMSA, and I strongly hypothesize that your son will be typically-developing after these metals are out of his brain."

I thanked the doctor and hung up the phone, then grabbed Luke in a bear hug, twirled him around the room and buried my face against his shoulder. Tears coursed down my cheeks as my mind flashed to the peaceful look on Luke's twin's face as he took his final breath. I shuddered to think that if my sweet baby hadn't sacrificed his life, we would have never known what was really wrong with Luke, and he would've been shrouded in an autistic fugue for the rest of his life.

Two weeks later, school started back up. Luke was now eight years old. His teachers were true to their word and kept him back in the second grade, with the same teachers, but all new classmates.

Since continuing the DMSA under this new doctor, though, Luke's attention span increased and his hyperactivity dwindled to a calm demeanor. Gone were the days I had to chase him down in the streets, thank goodness, and he was able to stay on task and complete his work without too much prompting.

But his diarrhea remained unresolved. No over-the-counter medicine I gave him even began to touch it. I had started Luke on the dairy-free, gluten-free diet after the doctor from Atlanta had mentioned it, starting with the dairy. But Luke squawked loud and long, sounding like one of those chickens in our yard, when I tried to take his pizza away from him. I just didn't have the heart to take away something that gave him so much joy, so after the doctor fired me, I scrapped the dairy-free/gluten-free diet.

Six months after the latest round of DMSA the doctor from Portland called. "Great news!" he chirped. "We can discontinue the DMSA. No further treatment."

"That's wonderful news, indeed," I cried. "I never thought I'd see the day."

My tone sobered as I lowered my voice. "I forgot to mention it to you before, but Luke has intractable diarrhea. He's had it since he was started on all those antibiotics all those years ago, and I haven't been able to clear it up."

"GI issues such as diarrhea and constipation are very common with kids who have autistic tendencies, though no one really knows why," the doctor replied. "I'll be happy to work up Luke's diarrhea and try to find out where it's coming from."

I sighed into the phone. "The doctor who fired me said something about leaky gut and malabsorption. We got the malabsorption resolved, but Luke still continues to have the diarrhea."

"Leaky gut's a very murky condition; one that's fraught with controversy. Since your son has had diarrhea for all these years, a gastroenterologist may be needed to scope him to rule-out a disease process. If a GI doctor is unable to find anything wrong with him, then we can proceed with treating a potential leaky gut. How does that sound to you?"

I agreed with the doctor's plan of care and hung up the phone, the cogs in my brain turning. I turned on my computer and read everything I could find about autism and GI issues on the internet. I learned that, according to *Medical News Today*, kids on the autism spectrum were six to eight times more apt to experience GI problems such as diarrhea and constipation than their typically-developing peers. The more severe the GI problems, the worse the behavior. It's theorized that autistic kids have inappropriate immune response, which causes inflammation, as well as altered bacteria in the gut. The gut and behavior appear to be tied together, though it's not understood how. For instance, a person with a gluten intolerance is more likely to have autism-like traits.[7]

In my research, one doctor's name kept popping up; a "world-famous" gastroenterologist based in New York City.

This doctor claimed he could help kids lose some of their autistic traits. He theorized that autism started in the gut, which made sense, since everything I read on the subject stated that the gut is crucial in the role of regulating the immune system.

I made an appointment for Luke to see this doctor, and it was agreed that the doctor would perform a colonoscopy on Luke to determine where the diarrhea was coming from.

Just before the new year, Luke and I left for the airport. We stopped on the way at Gary's office so that Luke could see his dad for a few minutes. Also, I wanted to let Gary know what was going on, since he was paying for everything.

I had just pulled into the parking lot when I saw Gary get into a car that looked eerily familiar. I craned my neck to see who was driving, and caught a flash of long, honey hair as they drove off.

The babysitter.

My heart flopped over and felt like it was being squeezed by a vise. I started hyperventilating as tears choked me, making me gasp for air. I laid my head upon the steering wheel and squeezed my eyes shut in an effort to block out the horrifying image.

I felt a hand on my arm and looked up to see Luke gazing at me with a wizened look — well beyond his years. I felt my face crumple as I stared into his fathomless brown eyes, and I gathered him in my arms, crying into the comfort of his shoulder.

"I'm so sorry, baby," I whispered. "Sorry that I picked such a lowly worm for a husband, who turned out to be a rotten husband and even more rotten father."

I wiped my eyes and sniffled. "But you wouldn't be here if I hadn't, so it's worth it; because you're the best thing that ever happened to me, and I love you so very much."

Luke nodded once and touched my hand. I cherished his gesture for the gift it was.

I grasped Luke's hand and managed a shaky smile. "Looks like it's me and you, kiddo. We're in this together. Through thick and thin. We have each other, and that's all that matters."

I straightened my spine, took a deep breath, then cried, "Onward to New York City!"

The doctor in New York City was a short, wiry man with thinning brown hair that had been combed over a bald spot. His intelligence crackled from brown eyes that peered at me behind silver-framed glasses.

The doctor frowned and looked past my shoulder as Luke and I entered his office. "Where's your husband?" he barked. "Didn't you tell me you're married to a doctor?"

I felt my bottom lip tremble as I struggled to contain a sob. Bowing my head, I stared at my shoes. "He was, uh, otherwise occupied."

The doctor's sharp gaze assessed my splotchy face and watery eyes, then moved down to the tent dress and tights I wore. He cocked his head and stared at me. "Let me guess. He left you for a younger woman."

"If you can call a girl, barely out of her teens, a woman, " I blurted as I sank into a chair and began to twist my fingers in the hem of my dress.

"It's tough getting older," the doctor growled. "We tend to do stupid things to prove that we're still attractive, and end up regretting it later in life."

"Oh, so you did the same thing," I snorted.

The doctor grimaced and turned his attention to Luke. "We're going to work up your son's diarrhea." He picked up a jug of liquid and handed it to me. "He needs to drink all of this today, and we'll scope him in the morning."

The next morning, I had Luke at the endoscopy center as the doctor had ordered. The nurses bustled about, helping Luke into a gown, and placed him on a stretcher. They draped a sheet over him and started an IV on him.

Just as they wheeled Luke off, he looked up at me, so small and pitiful on that stretcher, and asked, "Am I going to die?"

"Oh no, Luke!" I cried. "I would never let you die. I love you too much!"

I was just able to reach down and kiss him on his forehead before they wheeled him off to the endoscopy room. I stumbled to a chair after he left and bent my head into my hands, my shoulders shaking as sobs wracked my body.

How did it get to this? What had I done to my son?

I cursed Gary for insisting on buying that ridiculous farm, where all our misery started. The dog abandoned us and was never there to enjoy it, much less take care of it, anyway.

I let the tears flow until there were no more left, then leaned my head against the cushion. I reminded myself there was no point in wasting time looking back. I knew that I was doing everything in my power to help my son get better, and I took comfort in that. Whatever happened, good or bad, I was doing the best that I possibly could.

No regrets in life. Ever!

With that thought running through my head, I closed my eyes and dozed off until I felt a hand on my shoulder.

My eyes popped open and I jolted upright in my chair. "What's wrong! Where's Luke?" I cried. I shook my head as I scrambled to get my bearings.

The doctor smiled as he leaned over me. "Luke's fine. He's in the recovery room. Would you like to see him?"

"Let's go!" I said as I jumped out of my chair, tripping over myself in my haste to get to my son.

Luke was sitting up in his stretcher as we entered the recovery room, a nurse flanked on either side of him. One of the nurses, a woman with gray hair swept into a bun and wearing horn-rimmed glasses attached to a chain that dangled against her care-worn face, was sliding Luke's pants onto one of his legs.

"He can dress himself," I said.

The nurse gave me a stricken look. "I'm sorry, I was just trying to help, since he's …" She gave Luke a sidelong glance then lowered her voice, "*autistic*, you know, and can't take care of himself."

I felt myself bristle as that dreaded word reached my ears. "Regardless of what label he has, I'm trying to teach him independence. He's very capable of dressing himself."

I forced a smile, softened my tone and added, "Thanks for caring, though."

I reached down and encompassed Luke in my arms, breathing in the scent of baby shampoo as I nestled against his hair. "I'm so happy to see you," I murmured.

The doctor tugged at my arm. "Why don't you come into my office and let's discuss my findings. The nurses will keep an eye on your son while we're gone."

The doctor led me into a small, windowless room, its walls hidden behind bookshelves filled with thick tomes. A large desk dominated the room, with charts and papers stacked at precarious angles. He indicated a metal chair that faced the desk as he eased into a chair behind it.

He pushed the glasses against the bridge of his nose, cleared his throat, then said, "Your son has enterocolitis."

I jolted upright in my seat and gasped, "What's enterocolitis?"

"Enterocolitis is inflammation of the colon, most notably the lining of the colon."

"How did he get that?" I asked.

"It's unclear at this point, though some believe that excessive antibiotics kill the good bacteria that helps break down and digest food, which allows the bad bacteria to take over and release toxins in the body, which damages the inner lining of the colon. This gut dysbiosis, as it's called, causes inflammation, which in turn causes the symptoms such as the bloating and diarrhea that you mentioned."

The doctor shrugged and added, "Antibiotics and gut dysbiosis is a controversial subject, one that is met with scorn by much of the medical profession. There's speculation that taking probiotics may help restore normal flora in the gut, but that has not been proven, therefore, that remains controversial as well."

I nodded as the doctor's words settled into my brain. "Luke had many antibiotics over the years, sad to say. So how do we treat this enterocolitis?"

"Corticosteroids." The doctor clicked his pen and reached for a pad of paper. "I'm writing a prescription for Prednisone …"

I shook my head so hard I saw stars, cutting the doctor off as I shouted, "You're not putting my son on steroids! There's no way! Do you realize the side effects that come with taking steroids?"

I raised a shaky hand and ticked them off on my fingers. "The auto-immune disorders, depression, weight gain and the potential for liver damage. Not to mention, steroids mask the underlying cause, making it more difficult to find out what's causing the inflammation. And do you not recall me sharing with you that Luke wanted to kill himself after taking drugs that his liver couldn't break down because of the damage to his liver from those heavy metals? Isn't depression one of the side effects of steroids?"

I felt a chill go down my spine as I recalled the time Luke had told me that he wanted to kill himself, and suppressed a shudder. "No, no, no and *no*, again," I declared with an emphatic shake of my head with each "no."

The doctor closed his pen, leaned back in his chair and gave me a steely look. "Then I'm afraid I'm going to have to terminate your son's care. Find yourself another doctor."

I leaned forward and gripped the doctor's desk, my eyes wild. "You mean you're firing us, just like that? We can't even discuss other treatment options?"

The doctor stood and towered over his desk. "Just like *that*. I've had a very good success rate helping kids like your son get better, but I need compliance on the parents' end, not some Dr. *mom* who believes the quackery on the internet, then acts like she knows better than a board-certified doctor who spent years studying and practicing this disease. So, it's either let me be the doctor and you be the patient's mom, and your son will take the steroids that I prescribe for him, or find another doctor."

The doctor folded his arms across his chest and lifted a brow, as if waiting for an answer.

I stood and fumbled for my purse, then said in a cold voice, "The cows will come home first."

With a sweep of his arms, the doctor showed me the door and closed it with a resounding thud in my wake.

I gathered Luke and proceeded to our hotel, my mind awhirl. *Fired by not one, but two doctors. That's gotta be some*

kind of record. But we'll keep soldiering onward. Quitting is
not an option.

Luke and I spent New Year's Eve in a hotel overlooking Central Park. I stood at the window watching snow flurries pelt the pane as the midnight hour approached. The sounds of frenzied voices counting down the final seconds carried across the frosty night.

A roar erupted as fireworks lit the sky in a kaleidoscope of vibrant colors. I turned to gaze at Luke, snuggled in his bed, the sound of his breathing comforting to my soul.

"Happy New Year, baby," I whispered to Luke's sleeping form. "I promise I'll do everything in my power to get you well and make your life better."

I turned back to the window and rested my forehead against the cool glass, struggling to rise above the overwhelming despair that threatened to engulf me. *Traded in by a girl half my age. At some point I must find the courage to leave that two-timing snake of a husband. But right now, I need to focus on what's important, and that's taking care of Luke and continuing the fight to get him well. Then, and only then, will I turn my attention to taking care of my own needs.*

I raised my eyes to the cloud-laden sky, straightened my shoulders, my voice strong and clear as I spoke aloud. "My resolution for the new year is to get Luke well, then divorce Gary."

Calmed by a sense of resolve, I got ready for bed.

Chapter 9

Luke and I returned from the disastrous encounter with the "world-famous" gastroenterologist in New York City, dejected but not defeated. At least we had a diagnosis for Luke's diarrhea. The next step was finding an alternative to the steroids that the doctor had tried to put him on.

I turned to my trusty friend, the internet, for guidance. I found a holistic doctor in Montreal, Canada who claimed to have success in treating enterocolitis by using natural supplements without the side effects of steroids.

Buoyed by a feeling of hopefulness I called the number listed on the doctor's website. A female with a heavy French accent greeted me on the phone and answered the questions I bombarded her with. I was impressed with her intelligence, as well as her patience with me, and scheduled an appointment to see the doctor.

The doctor's office was tucked into a cobbled-stoned street jutting off of Old Montreal, a neighborhood founded by the French settlers in 1642. Luke and I dodged slushy drifts of snow as we approached the Gothic Revival building, a finial atop its steep roof spiraling toward the cloudless sky.

The doctor was tall and lean, with black curly hair. He sported a Hermes scarf around his neck, giving him a *je ne sais quoi* that made me feel at ease with him. He shook my hand, then Luke's, his gaze lingering on my son.

"I understand you are wanting an alternative to steroids," the doctor said in a lilting French accent as he ushered us to a seat.

I scanned the rows of important-looking degrees on the wall behind the doctor's desk before turning my attention to him. "Yes sir," I replied. "I'm afraid of steroids."

"As well you should be," the doctor said. He crossed his long legs and leaned back in his chair. "Steroids mask the underlying cause instead of addressing and fixing it."

"That's what I tried to tell the last doctor who fired me!" I gasped.

The doctor flashed me a smile. "Most conventional doctors, like this doctor in New York City, are trained to treat a symptom. They aren't trained to find the underlying cause and remove it, as holistic doctors, such as myself, are trained to do. We're trained not only in conventional medicine, which is treating the symptom, but also in holistic medicine, which is finding the underlying cause of the symptom and removing it. That's the big difference between conventional medicine and holistic medicine."

I leaned forward in my chair, mesmerized by his words.

"Take for instance, Luke's enterocolitis," the doctor said. "A conventional doctor sees inflammation and wants to treat that inflammation with Prednisone, which is the standard treatment for inflammation. He's not interested in what's causing that inflammation; he's more interested in alleviating the symptoms that go with that inflammation, such as diarrhea and abdominal pain. But us holistic doctors look for what's causing that inflammation and work on eliminating it. We remove the cause of the inflammation instead of suppressing the symptoms with Prednisone, which can lead to further disease processes, such as auto-immune disorders, if taken long-term."

The doctor paused as if coming up for air, then continued. "I'm going to put Luke on a treatment plan that I believe will stop the inflammation as well as the diarrhea. I have found in my practice that most kids on the autism spectrum have sensitivities to dairy and gluten, as well as sugar."

I nodded. "The doctor who treated Luke for his heavy metals told me the same thing. I took Luke off of dairy for about a week and didn't see any difference, so I gave up on it."

"Those heavy metals, along with all of those antibiotics, damaged the lining of Luke's gut. Based on that knowledge, and the intractable diarrhea, it's safe to say that Luke has developed sensitivities to dairy and gluten. Also, sugar inhibits the growth of good bacteria and causes an overgrowth of harmful bacteria, which leads to gut dysbiosis, or leaky gut. I propose that we eliminate these from his diet, starting with one at a time. Let's start with dairy, since it's easier to remove from the diet than gluten and sugar."

"But his pizza," I lamented, glancing over at Luke who was bent over a table, putting a puzzle together. "I hate to see him have to go without what he loves so much. He already suffers enough."

"Many times, we crave what we have sensitivities to," the doctor said. "Some companies are starting to cater to the needs of the dairy-free/gluten-free population, and are introducing dairy-free cheese that's as delicious as the real thing. Here in Canada we have long realized the inflammation that gluten causes and offer gluten-free pizza crust at all the pizza establishments."

The doctor scribbled in Luke's chart, then handed me a piece of paper. "I have all of the instructions written down here. Remove all dairy from Luke's diet, and give it two weeks to get out of his system. Learn to read labels. If it says it has whey in it, then it has dairy in it, and lactose-free does not mean dairy-free. It needs to say 'dairy-free' on the label, preferably in a dedicated dairy-free facility. After Luke has been dairy-free for at least two weeks, then it'll be time to remove the gluten. That may be a little trickier. Wheat-free does not mean gluten-free. It needs to say 'gluten-free' on the label. That needs to be from a dedicated gluten-free facility as well. After all gluten is out of your son's diet, then you can tackle sugar, which, from my understanding, is pervasive in your American diet. This includes all forms of sugar, including fruit and all artificial sweeteners except stevia. Stevia is a low glycemic sugar extracted from a plant found in Paraguay that doesn't raise the blood sugar or cause gut dysbiosis."

I stared at the paper the doctor had given me, my head spinning. "This looks too difficult."

The doctor smiled at me. "It's going to be a learning process. But once you get used to reading labels, it won't be nearly as daunting as it seems now. Luke's body will thank you for it."

The doctor got up and crossed the room, pausing before a row of shelves brimming with bottles of different sizes. He plucked one from the shelf and returned to his desk, then handed me the bottle.

"Activated quercetin," I said as I studied the label. "What's this?"

"That's your answer to Prednisone," the doctor replied. "We'll start Luke off on two capsules per day in the morning at breakfast."

"What is it?" I asked.

"It's a bioflavonoid that comes from the skins of red grapes. It's also found in blueberries, kale, green tea and tomatoes. It's a pigment that gives them their deep color. It's activated by bromelain, which is an enzyme. Together, they form a powerful anti-inflammatory that doesn't have the side effects that the corticosteroids do. Taking two capsules a day, along with the dairy-free/gluten-free /sugar-free diet should decrease Luke's inflammation, and stop the diarrhea."

The doctor was across the room again in two strides and returned with another bottle. "I'm also adding a probiotic, which will replace the good bacteria that was destroyed by all those antibiotics."

"The doctor in New York City did say something about probiotics and leaky gut, though he didn't sound very convinced about it," I said.

"Leaky gut is something most doctors aren't taught in medical school," the doctor said. "So, it's met with a lot of skepticism. Basically, leaky gut is permeability of the lining of the GI tract; the gut, so to speak. You see, the lining of the gut acts as a barrier; it allows the absorption of tiny molecules, such as nutrients and electrolytes, and protects the body from foreign invaders, such as toxins and bad bacteria. When the barrier is damaged, and the main culprits are gluten, sugar, antibiotics and toxins, it allows the bad guys, the toxins and the bad bacteria, to get into the blood stream. When that happens, the immune system attacks these foreign invaders, which causes the inflammation that Luke has. That inflammation causes food sensitivities and allergies, as well as auto-immune disorders."

The doctor tapped the bottle of probiotics. "This is what Luke needs to take to restore the normal permeability in his gut, along with the removal of gluten, dairy and sugar. These probiotics will work to counteract his leaky gut, and repair the gut barrier by basically killing the bad bacteria and replacing it with the good bacteria, thus restoring the normal flora the body needs to function at an optimal state."

The doctor reached across his desk and handed me the bottle. "I'm sending you home with this bottle, but when you go to buy another bottle, just remember to make sure to get dairy-free probiotics. Make sure it says 'dairy-free' on the label. Also, be sure to get probiotics that are at least fifty billion CFUs, with at least ten different strains."

The doctor lifted a finger, as if he had just thought about something. "Oh, by the way. The probiotics may cause a die-off reaction, such as brain fog, muscle aches, headaches, rashes, fever or chills. It just means that the probiotics are killing the bad guys, and the body is trying to get rid of the dying bad guys, which produces toxins. It shouldn't last more than three to seven days."

"Whew! So much to remember," I cried, making a dramatic sweep of my hand across my forehead. "And we're very familiar with the die-off by now."

The doctor's smile lit up his eyes, the startling blue a contrast to his raven curls. "I'm sure you'll figure it all out easily enough. You've done a remarkable job so far."

He glanced over at Luke, who, by this time, was reading one of the books that had been scattered across the table. "I don't see a whole lot wrong with him."

I beamed. "We've come a long way, but it's been a long, hard road to travel with a few casualties along the way, namely my marriage."

A sympathetic look flitted across the doctor's face. "I hear that a lot in dealing with families of autistic children. It takes a special person to be able to deal with the challenges of raising a special needs child."

"My husband said I've changed from the sweet country girl he married to a strong, independent woman who doesn't need him anymore, except for his money," I said, fighting a quivering that arose in my voice. "But I had to become strong so that I could fight for Luke, since he wasn't able to do it himself, and Luke's dad wasn't willing to. I tried to involve my husband in every aspect of Luke's care and elicit his opinion on everything. But he wasn't interested. Instead, he just hid under a rock; or in his case, fled to his office and abandoned us."

"You're Luke's greatest advocate," the doctor said. "Just keep fighting the good fight, and I believe Luke will lead a relatively normal life. He may never be perfect, but he'll be healthier, as well as a productive member of society."

"Perfect is boring anyway," I said with a laugh. "Quirky is much more interesting. I'll gladly take that."

I left that doctor's office with a spring to my step that I didn't realize still existed in me. That night I took Luke to one of those pizza parlors that the doctor had mentioned, and ordered us a large gluten-free pizza with dairy-free cheese. We both chowed down, smacking our lips after every bite.

And, guess what … it *was* delicious!

Chapter 10

I removed all dairy from Luke's diet as soon as we got home from Canada. It really wasn't that hard once I set my mind to it. I just learned to read labels very carefully, and even taught Luke how to read the labels of everything that we bought in the store.

In place of milk, we used chocolate almond milk, which Luke loved. For butter, we used Fleischmann's unsalted margarine, which is supposed to be dairy-free, and he tolerated very well. Though we could not find a dairy-free cheese in our small town that Luke would eat, he learned to eat his beloved pizza with a gluten-free crust and without cheese, and was happy to have that.

It was during that time that I started Luke on the activated quercetin and the probiotics. He did have the die-off reaction the doctor in Canada had mentioned, though it wasn't as bad as the reaction to the DMSA or the milk thistle. Plus, we had the activated charcoal to soak up the dying toxins, so that helped reduce the die-off symptoms a lot.

A few weeks after we took away the dairy, we tackled the gluten. Taking gluten out of Luke's diet was much more challenging, as we found out in a hurry that it's pervasive in the American diet, and may be hidden in the form of "natural flavors," as well as processed sauces.

Also, as I learned from the doctor, wheat-free doesn't mean gluten-free. I had the owner of the lone health food store in our town argue with me over that one. He insisted that his products were all gluten-free, though on the packages it clearly stated "wheat-free." I advised him in as polite a way as possible that he needed to do his research on that subject. He promptly escorted me from the premises and told me not to return.

I had to get most all of Luke's gluten-free food from the health food store, including his bread, crackers, pasta, waffles and pancake mix, so I had to find another health food store fast. I found one in Atlanta that was well-stocked with what he needed, and with a knowledgeable staff. After our first time going there, a weekend trek into Atlanta became part of our routine. Luke and I would pile into the car and make a fun day of it, stopping along the way at one of the many hiking trails that snaked throughout the foothills.

I became bold in my endeavors and bought a bread machine. I tried to make Luke's bread myself with gluten-free flour that I got from the health food store, but he gagged on it the first time he bit into it, and refused to take another bite. I had to end up feeding it to the chickens.

Yes, the health food store was expensive. But I felt that we made up for the expense by cooking at home and avoiding restaurants more often, and the benefits to Luke's health outweighed the cost of the health food store.

When we did eat out it was usually at McDonald's, which was one of Luke's favorite places to eat. I would ask for hamburger patties with no bun and French fries, and Luke would be ecstatic as he scarfed them down, laden with ketchup. We found that McDonald's was one of the few safe fast food restaurants, as most of the other places we tried, we found out that their fries were coated in wheat.

Two weeks after we took the gluten out of Luke's diet, we went to work on removing sugar. That proved to be a difficult endeavor, as Luke loved his ketchup.

But I had noticed that every time after eating ketchup, he would have incontinent diarrhea. I never understood how he wasn't able to feel it coming on and get to the bathroom in time. After researching the matter, I found out that sugar triggered IBS in Luke, or irritable bowel syndrome. The symptoms of IBS, including abdominal cramps and diarrhea, can come on so suddenly that one doesn't have time to get to the restroom. So that was a huge source of humiliation for Luke.

Luke learned to eat his French fries without ketchup, and the cakes and cookies went along the wayside, as well. About a week after throwing the ketchup bottle in the trash, Luke's diarrhea stopped as if a dripping faucet had been fixed. Along with it, went the smell that had lingered on him, a musty odor that had oozed out of his pores, and had followed him around like a stealthy shadow.

Oddly enough, it was after removing the offending foods from Luke's diet that he stopped walking on his toes ... around the same time that his diarrhea stopped.

Did the food sensitivities cause Luke's toe-walking? I went to Google Scholar to find answers. The latest research showed that 41% of children aged five with a neuropsychiatric label or developmental delay walk on their toes, as opposed to 2% of typically-developing children, though there is no discernable underlying cause.[8]

In other words, no one really knows why autistic kids walk on their toes.

There is growing evidence, though, that gluten sensitivity can be the culprit behind neurological conditions with unknown causations.[9] And since the central nervous system affects a person's gait, it stands to reason that gluten sensitivity could be attributed to toe-walking, or any food sensitivity for that matter, including dairy and sugar.

After we had implemented the gluten-free/dairy-free/sugar-free diet, I found digestive enzymes at the health food store that allegedly helps the digestive tract break down proteins that the body has trouble breaking down otherwise; proteins such as dairy and gluten. He would take three or four enzymes if he was going to have a cheat day at a restaurant that didn't have a gluten-free menu. He didn't have an episode of diarrhea after the meal, though I did notice that he would be high on his toes, pacing the floor and flapping his hands for the next day or two.

Were those few days of increased autistic tendencies after a cheat day worth it? To Luke, it meant that he was a regular kid eating regular food like all of the other regular kids, even if it was just for the day. So, to him, yes, one cheat day every few weeks was worth the next few days of atypical behavior. We just made sure that we timed the cheat day for the weekend, when there was nothing going on for the next few days.

The dairy-free/gluten-free/sugar-free diet became a staple in Luke's life, along with the activated quercetin, the probiotics and the milk thistle. Luke tolerated the diet well, and stopped fussing about missing his cheese doodles and ketchup after his bowels started to normalize.

About three months after Luke had been on his diet, I had just dropped him off at school. I was just about to drive off when one of his teachers, a petite blonde who had been standing on the curb doing pick-up duty, waved her arms in the air and shouted at me.

I screeched to a stop, muttering under my breath, "Uh oh, here comes trouble."

She ran up to the driver's side of the car and tapped on the window. "Can I talk to you for a second?" she asked in a breathless voice, sounding as if she had just run a marathon.

I felt my innards quiver as I pasted a smile on my face and rolled down the window. "If it's about how much school Luke has missed, I have an answer for …"

The teacher cut me off. "It's nothing to do with how much school Luke's missed. I want to know what you've done. There's something different about Luke, but I can't quite put my finger on it."

I cringed as my mind raced to figure out what travesty Luke had committed. "Um. What's he done this time?"

The teacher snapped her fingers then cried, "That's it! That's what's different about Luke. I haven't had to send him to the principal's office for fighting or put him in the time-out room lately."

She stuck her head through the window, her minty breath blowing in my face. "Have you put him on a new ADD medicine? Is that what you've done? He's so much calmer now, so you must have put him on something."

My mouth hung open as I stared at the teacher. "You mean to tell me that you're saying something positive about Luke for a change?"

The teacher guffawed as if we were best friends sharing a joke, instead of the nemesis she had become the past two years. "Well, yeah! Whatever you're doing, keep doing it. Who knows, Luke may even pass this time. Second time's the charm, they say."

The teacher wagged her fingers at me and sashayed off, leaving me floundering for words.

A sense of triumph surged through my body. I wanted to sing. I wanted to dance. I wanted to shout from the rooftops.

There's hope for my baby after all!

Chapter 11

The school year came to a thankful close. On a drizzling spring day, the teachers, speech therapist, principal and myself huddled around a table in the conference room, deciding Luke's fate. Or, at least, they did and I sat in a corner and made myself as small as possible, bracing myself for the onslaught I knew was coming.

I always hated these IEP, or individualized education program, meetings, as the team went around the table telling me how bad Luke was. As if I didn't already know that. But the IEP is a necessary document for kids that need to receive support and services in order to be successful in school. It's sort of like a blueprint for passing the school year.

But this time, the meeting was different. The teachers shuffled papers importantly then looked around the room at each other, as if waiting for someone to start.

The ticking of the clock was the only sound in the room as we stared at each other. After what seemed an eternity the principal looked at her watch, then cleared her throat. "Alright, let's get started. I've got another meeting after this. Who wants to go first?" She nodded at the blonde who had chased me down a few months ago. "Mary Beth, we'll start with you."

Mary Beth drummed her fingers against the table, shrugged her shoulders, then gazed at the woman to her right. "I got nothing. Susan, it's your turn."

The principal held up her hand and gawked at Mary Beth. "Hold it right there. What do you mean you 'got nothing'? This is the same child you've been either sending to me all year, or been putting in the time-out room."

The principal paused and rubbed her chin. "Come to think of it, though, I haven't seen him in the office lately."

"That's what I'm trying to tell you!" Mary Beth cried. "There's nothing to report. These past few months, Luke's been sitting quietly in his chair and minding his own business, and doing his work. I haven't had to get onto him once. I swear, his mom has put him on something and hasn't told us about it."

All heads swiveled towards me. I sat up in my chair and said, "Don't look at me. I haven't put him on anything. Luke and I just cleaned up his diet and put him on some supplements."

They all started talking at once, sounding like a bunch of cackling hens. The principal silenced them with a wave of her hand. "Alright, then. Are we all in agreement that Luke has progressed enough to move him up to the third grade?"

A chorus of "Ayes" filled the room.

"He's ready for regular class in the third grade," Mary Beth chirped.

The principal looked at the other women in the room. "Susan? Amy? Kim? Are you all in agreement with Mary Beth's assessment?"

The other teachers nodded in unison.

The speech therapist, a Hispanic woman with eyes that emanated the warmth of molten chocolate, raised her hand. "I'd like to keep Luke in speech therapy so that we can work on improving his expressive language, which he continues to struggle with."

The principal turned to me and gave me a begrudging look. "Congratulations. Whatever you've done, it appears to have worked. We're moving Luke up to the third grade. He'll be in regular classes, but we'll pull him out for speech therapy, so he'll still have an IEP."

I felt my jaw go slack as my mind scrambled to process such good news, for a change. "I'm flabbergasted. I never thought I'd see this day." I felt my mouth split into a wide grin. "I thank you all so much for all you've done for Luke."

The bell rang as we all stood up. After saying a hasty goodbye, I bolted out of the room and made a beeline for Luke's class. The kids were spilling into the hallway as I elbowed my way into the classroom.

I swooped Luke into my arms and planted a kiss on his cheek. "Celebrations are in order!" I crowed. "How about we mosey on down to the California Pizza Kitchen and get some of their scrumptious gluten-free pizza? What say you, little buddy?"

Luke's eyes lit up like firecrackers, and he nodded his head so hard that he looked like one of those bobbing dogs.

We skipped down the hallway, hand in hand; at that moment in time, just two happy-go-lucky souls with not a care in the world.

Chapter 12

That summer, instead of leaving Luke alone on the farm, with only the chickens and cows for company, as well as an old mule named Clyde, I decided to send him to his first summer camp. I had read about an adaptive camp in Colorado in an autism parenting magazine, and my interest was piqued.

Unsure of what an "adaptive camp" meant, I called the number provided and talked to a delightful woman at the camp. She explained to me that they used adaptive equipment to help kids with developmental disabilities learn how to ride a horse, kayak, rope-climb, ski and ride a bicycle in a safe environment. They also boasted a heated swimming pool, a gym and extensive hiking trails.

The camp director added that they taught life skills such as tying their shoes, dressing and caring for themselves, washing their clothes and cleaning their rooms. The staff also worked on social skills by having campfires, sing-alongs and games that encouraged the kids to interact with each other.

The director went on to explain that the campers stayed in log cabins, with a ratio of four campers to one counselor. The more severely-affected kids had a counselor to themselves.

The kitchen served meals based on the individual child's diet. For example, since Luke was on a gluten-free/dairy-free/sugar-free diet, the kitchen staff would be careful to prepare his food away from the food that contained dairy or gluten. They would also have him sit with the other kids who were on the same diet, to help reduce any chance of cross-contamination.

As I listened to the camp director gush about the advantages of summer camp for kids with autism, I felt my heart race as excitement bubbled inside of me. That is, until the director mentioned the cost.

I gagged on the bile that rushed into my throat. "Did you just say $1000 a *week?*" I sputtered into the phone.

"Yes, I did," the director said with a tinkling laugh. "But that includes all meals and lodging, as well as activities. And, you have my word, we'll take very good care of your son. It's a wonderful opportunity for him to learn how to adapt to the real world, and be able to cope when he's faced with being on his own."

That last statement sealed the deal. I shuddered at the thought of my not being around for Luke, but I knew that the day would come, and we needed to be prepared for it.

The cogs in my head turned as I weighed the pros and cons of sending Luke off to camp. Sure, one thousand dollars was a lot of money, but if Luke learned how to take care of himself and become able to live independently, then the money would be well worth the cost. Not only would a camp give Luke the opportunity to be around other children his age, but it would teach him valuable skills that would help him make his way in this world long after I was no longer around to take care of him. And since the camp was only a week long, it would give Luke a taste of freedom and independence, without being so long that it created homesickness.

My mind made up, I focused on how I was going to pay for it. I knew that Gary wasn't going to be happy about me dragging his son off across the country, and would squawk about the cost. In my mind, though, Gary wasn't in a position to make decisions about Luke's care, since he chose not to be a part of Luke's life.

I knew we had enough sky miles saved from our credit card, so our plane tickets would be free. The director told me there were hostels, or dorm-style hotels that were very low in cost, near the camp. That gave me a cheap place to stay, though I would have to sleep in a bunkbed in the same room with a bunch of rowdy college students. But that was a small sacrifice to make to ensure that Luke was getting the experience of a lifetime.

Luke made his displeasure at being sent off to camp quite apparent. He pitched fits for no reason, falling on the floor and flailing his arms and legs as if he was having apoplexy. I would just step over his squirming body and carry on with my business at hand. When that didn't work, Luke then resorted to whining and crying; long and loud, from the moment he dragged himself out of bed in the morning until he dropped from exhaustion at night. I would look over at him during one of his crying spells then shake my head.

"You're not even crying real tears, so you may as well stop being fake."

I managed to ignore his shenanigans for the most part, though I must admit his constant whining was grating on my nerves. But I kept telling myself that the camp was in his best interest, and that thought kept me calm in the midst of the tantrum storm.

We made the trek to Colorado a few weeks later, and pulled up to the camp just as the sun sank behind the mountains, bathing the snow-capped peaks in a purple sheen. The waning rays dappled a pristine lake tucked in the midst of a thick grove of evergreen trees, while log cabins dotted the shore. A stable jutted off to the side of a clearing, with the sound of horses whinnying carrying across the soft breeze.

The counselors, all whom appeared to be college students, were standing on the veranda of the office, which resembled a snow lodge, with exposed beams, large windows that mirrored the mountains and stone walls. The counselors smiled and waved at us as we pulled up to the circular driveway.

Luke had his seatbelt unbuckled and one foot out the door, a smile stretched across his face, before I even turned off the car.

"Luke, stop!" I cried. "Wait for me."

But Luke was off like a shot, heading in the direction of a girl with long blond hair that shimmered in the fading light. The girl, wearing a tee shirt with the camp logo on it, reached out her arms to Luke and he ran into them, embracing her as if they were long-lost buddies.

"It's time for you to go now," Luke called over his shoulder in my direction.

"Looks like they're making him a little *too* independent, already," I grumbled to myself as I lugged his suitcase toward the office.

"At least give me a hug goodbye," I hollered to Luke's retreating back.

Luke turned and gave me a perfunctory hug. I grabbed him and held onto him, savoring the moment, desperately fighting to hold in the tears.

"I'm gonna miss you, little buddy," I whispered into his hair.

Luke wriggled out of my grasp and grabbed the girl's outstretched hand, then called out to me, "You can go now. Later, gator."

The girl looked down at Luke and asked, "Would you like your mom to come see your cabin?"

"No, she's busy." Luke tugged on the girl's hand, and they took off in search of his cabin.

My bottom lip quivered as I watched my son leave me for the first time in his life, a portent of things to come crowding my head. I stumbled toward the car, and just dipped inside before the tears fell down my face. I cradled my head against the steering wheel and sobbed, my mind reeling.

Luke has been my life since the day he was born. I must learn to be on my own and have my own life, if I'm to survive when the day comes that he leaves me.

I wiped my eyes and started the ignition. "Oh well. Staying with a room full of rowdy college kids is a start," I said out loud.

I took a deep breath, squared my shoulders and drove off into the gathering gloom.

Chapter 13

The week of summer camp came to a thankful end. I was there as soon as they allowed the parents in the camp, so ready to see Luke again and go home.

The pretty, blond counselor brought Luke to the car, along with his luggage. He was clinging to the girl's hand as if it was a buoy in a churning sea.

I felt my heart race as I watched my son approach, tears welling in my eyes as an overwhelming rush of love for this child overcame me. I ran toward him, wrapped my arms around him and snuggled against his shoulder.

"I'm so happy to see you," I cried.

"Luke's an awesome kid," the girl gushed. "He learned to tie his shoes and ride a horse. We went skiing, hiking and swimming, and we even baked cookies. Gluten-free and sugar-free, of course."

The girl hugged Luke, then they high-fived and yelled in unison, "Later, gator!"

Luke got into the car amidst a chorus of "See you next summer!" from the counselors. He craned his neck and waved at them until they were a speckle on the distant horizon.

"It looks like you had a wonderful time," I said, as I eased the car down the mountain.

"Hmphh," was Luke's reply. He then leaned his head against the window and ignored me the rest of the way home, save for the occasional grunt.

The rest of that summer was uneventful. Luke and I worked on computer programs every day, such as reading and math skills, to keep him from regressing over the summer break. We also had the cousins over a few times, and would have fun with trivia and card games, which sharpened his memory skills.

Luke's ninth birthday came up right before school was to start. I took him and a friend from his school to Atlanta for pizza and video games.

This friend, a kid named Jake, who had been in the same class with Luke since kindergarten, was very good to Luke, and spent time with him when most of the other kids wouldn't. Jake lived with his grandparents deep in the foothills. He had a bit of a learning disability, and wasn't considered as bright as the other kids, but he was a good kid. Also, he was good to Luke, which warmed my heart towards him.

On this particular rainy night in August, I took Jake home after our night out in Atlanta, and watched him as he entered his home. After the door closed behind him, I turned to Luke and said, "Well, that was a lot of fun. Jake is such a wonderful friend."

Luke turned and smirked at me.

My jaw dropped as I stared at him. For, in that moment, *I knew.*

"There's nothing wrong with you," I whispered. "How long have you been faking it?"

Luke just looked at me and shrugged.

The next day I scheduled an appointment with a behavioral psychologist. The doctor, a woman with grey hair cut in a bob that framed her angular face, was thorough in her evaluation of Luke, and blunt in her assessment of him.

"Your son Luke is very smart, with an I.Q. of 119, which places him in the above-average range." She held up a hand at my gasp. "But he's also very manipulative." The doctor leaned back in her chair and folded her hands. "He's learned how to get his way by acting more severely autistic than he actually is. In fact, I wouldn't even place him on the autism spectrum. He has some expressive language deficits, but no discernible autistic traits. Therefore, I'm going to label him as having 'expressive language disorder.'"

The doctor eyed Luke, who was leaning back in his chair with his arms behind his head and one foot draped across his other leg, and wagged a finger at him. "Young man, I have to admire you for your skill in manipulating not only your mother, but your teachers as well. You've gamed the system by getting out of doing your work by acting dumb. But your gig is up now; you've been found out. It's time for you to step up to the plate and act like the fine young man you're capable of being."

A shadow of a smile tugged at the corner of Luke's mouth, though he remained quiet.

The doctor turned to me and smiled. "Congratulations, Mom. Whatever you've done, worked. Just stay strong and don't cave under Luke's manipulative tactics."

I clasped my hands and beamed at the doctor's words. "Thanks so much for those kind words, Doctor. I thought I'd never see the day. It's been a long, hard road to travel, with no guidance along the way, since no one really knows what causes autism. It's almost as if we're trailblazers in the world of autism."

"It's a mystery as to what's causing all of this autism," the doctor said with a shake of her head. "The school system is inundated with staggering cases of autism every year, and the medical profession is baffled as to what's causing this autism epidemic."

The doctor lifted a brow and smiled at me. "Maybe you should write a book about autism recovery, since your son appears to have recovered."

"Like anyone would believe that heavy metals cause autism," I laughed.

"All we have are educated guesses, anyway," the doctor said. "What's one more theory to throw out there? Your theory that heavy metal poisoning mimics autism does make sense."

I felt my face split into a wide grin as I stood up and draped an arm around Luke's shoulders. "It's as good of a guess as any," I said with a laugh.

I ruffled Luke's hair as we exited the doctor's office. "We're finally out of the woods. It's smooth sailing from here!"

The heavens must have shifted at my flippant remark, for my words came back to haunt me.

Chapter 14

The loss of Luke's short-term memory was the first sign that he was slipping back into his autistic fugue. I started noticing it about a year after Luke had his autism label removed by the behavioral psychologist.

Luke had just started the fourth grade, and began leaving his lunch bag on the kitchen counter as he shuffled out the door to school; the one thing he always guarded with his life and would never, ever forget. I called after him to come back and get his lunch, then he raced back into the house, huffing and puffing as if he had just finished a fifty-yard sprint.

After about the third time in a week that this happened, I scratched my head and muttered to myself, "What's going on with this kid?"

I shrugged, thinking that he was just a little stressed at school. But when Luke started running around the house screaming that he lost his iPad, I knew we had a problem.

One fall morning as we were getting ready for school, I heard what sounded like a herd of elephants stampeding down the hall. I darted out of my room, a toothbrush in one hand, to see Luke rummaging through the kitchen cabinets.

"What the …" I cried, staring at the pile of pots and pans scattered on the floor. "What're you doing, Luke?"

Luke ignored me, yanked open a drawer, and tossed hand towels as if he was throwing confetti at a parade.

I grabbed him by the shoulders and turned him around to face me. "Tell me what's wrong so that I can help you."

Luke's gaze slid to the side of my face, his jaw slack, "My backpack. It's missing."

I let go of his arm and pointed in the direction of the dining room table. "It's on the chair, where it always sits."

"Oh! Yes, it is," he cried, then ran over to the table, scooped up his backpack, then scurried out the door and jumped in the car.

Along the way to school, my stomach churned as my mind conjured all sorts of calamities explaining Luke's loss of memory. I felt the bile rise in my throat as visions of everything from early onset of Alzheimer's to, God forbid, brain cancer flitted through my head.

I raced into the house after I got home and called the doctor in Portland, forgetting that they were three hours behind me. I left a message with the doctor's answering service, then paced the floors, willing the clock to move faster.

Three hours later, the ringing of the phone startled me into action. I ran and snatched the phone off the counter, my body trembling when I heard the doctor's greeting.

"I think Luke's symptoms are coming back," I said in a shaky voice. "His short-term memory is gone, his eye contact is poor and his speech is regressing. And his teachers are asking me what I've done to him, saying they're going to put him back in all special needs classes; that he can't keep up with the kids in his class anymore."

"Has anything changed?" the doctor asked.

"I've been beating my brain about that," I said. "He's still on his gluten-free/dairy-free/sugar-free diet and taking his supplements. I haven't introduced any new foods lately. He takes his lunch to school every day, and I cook his meals, so he's not sneaking any food."

I heard what sounded like pages flipping, then the doctor asked, "You haven't been doing anymore renovations on your house or spraying with pesticides, have you? And you're filtering your water?"

"Nothing's changed," I said, a tinge of exasperation flooding my voice. "I use filtered water only, even for cooking. And I haven't touched my house, except to clean it, or used any pesticides. I've learned better than that the hard way."

"Though it's only a remote possibility that the heavy metals have returned, let's repeat the heavy metal challenge, just to rule that out," the doctor said. "I'm sending you a kit in the mail and when I get the results back, I'll call you."

The doctor lowered his voice until it was a soothing murmur. "Try not to worry about it. It's probably just a precursor to puberty. Luke's, what, nine now?"

"He just turned ten," I replied.

"Oh, my word, they do grow up so fast," the doctor chuckled. "Well, hang tight, get that heavy metal challenge done, and I'll talk to you in a few weeks."

A few weeks later, I looked down at the caller ID of my ringing phone and froze. My fingers fumbled to open my phone, then I managed to push a weak "hello" through lips rigid with fear.

"I'm afraid the heavy metals are back," the doctor said by way of greeting. "And with a vengeance. Your son's body is full of mercury and aluminum."

"How could that happen?" I gasped. "I thought his heavy metal toxicity was resolved, and that there was no further treatment."

The doctor's voice rose as exasperation punctuated his words. *"What's going on with this kid?* Why does his body keep storing heavy metals? Has he been getting vaccines lately? That's the only thing I can think of. But, still, even if he got vaccines, a person's body is supposed to be able to excrete heavy metals through the urine. The body is not supposed to hold onto heavy metals."

"Luke hasn't had a vaccine since we found out he had heavy metal poisoning, and he will never have another one," I said. "It's got to be coming from the environment."

"Well let's start another round of DMSA. In the meantime, keep a close eye on everything that comes into close proximity with your son … the food he eats, the water he drinks, even the deodorant he uses. Make sure that he only uses deodorant that doesn't contain aluminum. Also, make sure he doesn't eat fish, use antacids, eat anything processed or out of aluminum cans. Don't use aluminum foil or cook with aluminum pots and pans. Only cook with cast iron, ceramic, glass or stainless steel."

I swallowed a gulp. "Well, gee, we may as well go on one of those Neanderthal diets, then, and cook like the cavemen did," I said with a weak laugh.

"Except you can't drink the water these days," the doctor laughed. "Even purified water has been shown to have aluminum in it. It's not regulated by the FDA, so we're not sure how much is in there. Distilled water is supposed to be free of aluminum."

The doctor lowered his tone, and a sense of urgency crept into his voice. "There's growing evidence that aluminum, as well as mercury, are directly correlated with Alzheimer's. We really need to work on lessening our heavy metals burden, and it takes a lot of discipline to do that. Watch Luke's intake, get him started on the DMSA and we'll retest for metals after this round is finished."

The doctor paused for a second then added, "Keep your chin up. We're in uncharted territory with your son … like Lewis and Clark were back in the day."

"I just don't want to be the one who ends up killing himself," I said with a wry chuckle.

I hung up my phone, my head spinning and my spirits sagging. Just when we thought that we were out of the woods and following that mystical road to recovery, we found out that we went around in one gigantic circle, and were now back to where we started.

But I reassured myself by noting that Luke had speech now, which he didn't have when we first started, his ear infections were now a thing of the past, and his GI tract was much healthier. So, I stopped feeling sorry for myself and turned my focus toward getting the heavy metals out of Luke once again, and keeping them out this time.

The doctor started Luke back on the DMSA. Within a week, Luke's short-term memory returned, he was able to focus better and his speech flourished. Peace was restored in our household, and we hummed along for the next six months.

After that round of DMSA was finished, the doctor called and proclaimed Luke to be free of the heavy metals. "No further treatment," he announced.

"Famous last words," I laughed. "Let's keep our fingers crossed."

"To be honest, I've never treated a kid quite like Luke," the doctor said. "He's definitely a case study, and one from whom we can all learn. Those heavy metals did so much damage to his body that it's difficult to regulate it."

I choked back a sob as my mind flashed to Luke's twin. "He's so lucky to be alive, at least," I whispered. "I'm thankful for that above everything else."

I thanked the doctor for all he had done for Luke, and hung up the phone.

Luke finished the school year without much incident and went to his summer camp, which had become a summer staple in our lives. He was healthy and happy, with no discernable autistic traits, save the expressive language disorder.

He had lost the savant skills that he had displayed at such a young age, but his mind was sharp. His memory was remarkable; he always knew where he kept everything, and his recall was amazing to behold.

But after about a year of finishing the last round of DMSA, Luke started slipping away from me once again. His faltering short-term memory was the telltale sign. He once again began misplacing his backpack, books and even the new phone *Santa* had gifted him.

His weight mushroomed, until he was popping at the seams of his clothes. I'd have to drag him out of bed every morning, and keep him active during the day, or he would crawl back under his covers as soon as I turned my back.

I realized then that something was going on inside Luke's body; something that had eluded myself as well as the doctors who had treated Luke all this time. Something was causing Luke's body to store the heavy metals instead of excreting them.

But what?

I knew that if I could figure out the connection, I would then be able to get Luke well and *keep* him well. I squared my shoulders and went to work, reading everything about autism that I could get my hands on.

Whisperings of a link between autism and genetics was just beginning to reach my ears, specifically the MTHFR gene. The MTHFR gene was discovered as a result of the Human Genome Project of 2003, a thirteen-year collaboration of scientists from around the world studying the genetic composition of the human body.[10]

The MTHFR gene is responsible for methylation, or detoxifying pathways, which includes detoxifying heavy metals. Researchers found that the MTHFR gene mutation has the variants C677T and A1298C, which they have determined increases the risk of developing autism.[11]

I called the doctor as soon as I read the results of the study, my voice giddy with excitement. "I may have found out what's causing Luke to hold onto heavy metals." I cried. "Have you heard of the MTHFR gene mutation?"

The line was quiet for a moment as if the doctor was pondering that question. He then replied in a low tone, "This is a new frontier in medicine that I've not incorporated into my practice. So, I'd be lying to you if I told you that I'm an expert on it. There are some cutting-edge doctors who have jumped on the genetics bandwagon, so to speak. There's one in particular in Florida whom I would be happy to refer you to. I think you're on the right path, but I'm not qualified to treat such a complex case such as your son's in this new realm of genetic medicine."

I hung up with the doctor, feeling overwhelmed but not undaunted. Getting Luke well was the bane of my existence, and I would not stop until I had exhausted all avenues of recovery.

Chapter 15

Springtime in Florida with its swaying palm trees and salt-kissed breezes was a welcome respite from the cold, dreary North Georgia mountains. In our quest for answers, Luke and I found ourselves in Orlando, a sprawling mecca of entertainment parks and outlet malls.

The doctor, an Asian man wearing thick glasses, greeted Luke with a handshake and a wink. He then showed us to chairs as he eased himself behind his desk.

The doctor turned to me and held up a chart bulging with papers. "I took the liberty of getting a copy of Luke's medical records from his previous doctors. It appears that you've left no stone unturned in your journey to recover him. That's very commendable of you. You're a remarkable woman, and your son's very lucky to have you for a mom. Most parents would just take the advice of their doctor, accept the fact that their child has autism, and not pursue alternative methods for recovery."

I felt my body relax as the doctor's kind words washed over me. "Journey is quite the understatement," I chuckled. "It's been twelve years of emotional turmoil; like being on a gigantic roller coaster and not being able to get off. Some days Luke's so normal that you can't tell anything is going on with him, then other days he's acting very disabled and it's very evident that something is very wrong with him."

The doctor nodded. "I realize how frustrating that must be for you."

I pushed back a lock of hair that had fallen in my face and grimaced. "It drives me crazy. I wish that we could fix what's wrong with him and then go on with our lives. But just when we think we fixed what was wrong, something else comes along that turns our world upside down again."

I gestured towards Luke, who was bent over his phone. "His heavy metals keep coming back and I can't, for the life of me, figure out why. Also, his weight has ballooned over the past year, and I have no idea of what's caused it. Nothing has changed with his diet, and I get him out walking with me every day. He also stays in his bed all the time when he's not at school, and doesn't appear to have any energy."

"We'll do a full work-up on him and check his thyroid and adrenal glands levels." The doctor clicked his pen and scribbled in Luke's chart. "I'll have the lab technician draw some blood and we'll do a heavy metal challenge, then we can have a phone consult to go over the findings."

"I've been told that you're knowledgeable about genetics," I said. "Have you heard about the MTHFR gene?"

The doctor took off his glasses and gazed at me. "I consider myself quite learned in genetics and autism. There's been research indicating that the MTHFR gene is associated with autism, but as it stands now, they've not definitively isolated an autism gene."

"But you'll test Luke for the MTHFR gene?" I asked.

"I do have it checked as part of his work-up." The doctor arose from his chair and gestured toward the door. "Shall we get started by having his blood drawn now?"

I nodded my approval as I stood, then took Luke by the hand and followed the doctor down the hall and into the lab. After several stabs, the lab technician drew Luke's blood and we parted ways with the doctor, with promises to reconvene when the results came in.

A few weeks later the doctor called. "Your son has a heavy burden of mercury and aluminum in his body, and his adrenal glands are stressed. The thyroid studies came back normal, and he tested negative for the MTHFR gene mutation."

"From what I've read, a negative MTHFR doesn't rule out autism, though," I said.

"You're right," the doctor replied. "But based on my observation of your son and my knowledge of genetics, your son is *not* autistic. His body is burdened with heavy metals, which have caused extensive damage to his body. His adrenal glands are deteriorating, which is a direct result of heavy metal toxicity. On an interesting side-note though, I've read studies where patients with adrenal gland deterioration are unable to complain."

"Luke's never complained!" I gasped. "As much as I've put him through, he's yet to complain once."

"Let's schedule an appointment and get treatment started. We'll start him on a DMSA regimen, and we'll start him on Adrenal Stress, which should resolve his weight and lethargy issues. If the treatment isn't successful, then we'll send him to the Mayo Clinic."

"So, if Luke loses weight, gains energy and starts to complain, then we'll know the treatment is working," I laughed.

"Exactly," the doctor chuckled. "I'll transfer you to the receptionist to make an appointment, and then we'll get started on the treatment. See you in two weeks."

I spent the next few weeks poring over articles about heavy metals and detoxification. The more I read, the more convinced I became that something was blocking Luke's body from excreting heavy metals.

But what?

I wracked my brain until it was numb from exhaustion. It was such a maddening thought knowing that the answer lay buried in the new frontier of genetic medicine, but no one had discovered it yet. Sure, there was plenty of speculation and conjecture, but nothing proven; no evidence-based data to support these theories.

My eureka moment came to me a week later in the form of a phone call from my mom.

My dad had just been diagnosed with Alzheimer's.

I had learned in nursing school that the first sign of Alzheimer's disease is loss of short-term memory. The first sign that Luke's heavy metals were coming back was a loss of short-term memory. There had to be a connection. I just had to find out what it was.

According to the doctor in Portland, there was growing evidence that Alzheimer's is caused by heavy metals stored in the brain, most notably mercury and aluminum. Because of this, I was beginning to see a direct correlation between autism and Alzheimer's.

In my research I found that Alzheimer's is characterized by a mutation of the APOE gene. There are three different versions, or alleles, of the APOE gene: APOE2, APOE3 and APOE4. The E2 and E3 have cysteine, which in turn contains sulfhydryl, an organosulfur compound that has a great affinity for soft metals, such as mercury and aluminum. This means that the E2 and E3 can bind with heavy metals and detoxify them when they cross the blood-brain barrier.

The APOE4 allele, on the other hand, does not have the capability to detoxify the brain of heavy metals. Instead, it appears to store them, as increased mercury accumulation has been noted in brain tissue for people with the APOE4 allele, determining that the genetic make-up of APOE may play a part in mercury detoxification. It's been noted that APOE4 is a major risk factor for dementia, as well as abnormal cognitive development, such as autism [12]

Armed with my theory as to what causes autism (or, at least, a subset of it,) I approached the doctor at our next visit as if I was a PHD student presenting her dissertation.

"I believe that Luke has the double APOE4 gene," I ventured as soon as I sat across from the doctor. "Especially since I just found out that my dad has Alzheimer's. Luke's body isn't able to excrete heavy metals, and stores them in his brain instead, as well as other soft tissues in his body, causing memory issues, altered thought process and CNS abnormalities, which are symptoms of mercury toxicity. And there is research supporting the theory that the APOE4 gene has no ability to detoxify heavy metals from the brain."

The doctor removed his glasses and stared at me. "You may just be right," he replied after a long pause.

I felt my heart race as a wave of euphoria engulfed my soul, thrilled that the doctor didn't laugh in my face or, worse, call me a delusional fool and kick me out of his office. Erring on the side of caution, though, just in case he was thinking it, I squeaked, "Errr, I *am?*"

The doctor placed his glasses back on his face, cocked his head toward me and stroked his chin. "You have a very valid point there."

I leaned forward in my chair and asked, "Shall we test him for the APOE4 gene?"

The doctor waved a hand at me. "Let's just assume he has it. No need to test him for it. He's hard enough to stick as it is."

"So, we'll need something to keep the heavy metals out of him; something that he can take every day that's not as potentially as harmful as DMSA." I lifted a finger and added, "Oh, by the way, that Adrenal Stress is working miracles for

Luke. The scales today show that he's already lost ten pounds, and his energy level has skyrocketed."

The doctor smiled and nodded. "I'm very pleased to hear that. As for supplements to keep the heavy metals out, I've seen success with chlorella, cilantro and zeolite. I would go with the zeolite for your son, though."

I raised a brow. "*Zeolite?* I've never heard of it."

"Zeolite is a byproduct of volcanic ash, and is a very good chelator of heavy metals. It doesn't remove essential vitamins and minerals from the body like DMSA and EDTA do, so it's reputed to be gentle enough to take every day, as opposed to DMSA and EDTA, which have to be carefully monitored by a qualified doctor."

The doctor cast his eyes upon Luke and smiled. "Your son should be fine, and grow up to be a healthy, independent adult."

The doctor then stood and held out his hand across the desk to me. "Congratulations, Mom. Your idea to maintain a daily low-dose chelation therapy is a brilliant one, and worthy of the Nobel Prize."

I grasped the doctor's hand and shook it fervently. "I don't care about any Nobel Prize. I just want my son to grow up to be healthy, happy and independent. To me, that's recovery enough."

I went home from the doctor's office riding high on a wave of euphoria, so thrilled knowing that there were detoxifiers out there safe enough to take every day. I made a beeline for the computer as soon as I set my purse and keys on the kitchen counter and entered the word *zeolite.*

A frown creased my face as I read about it. According to Wikipedia, zeolite comes from the earth, which the doctor had mentioned. But what the doctor *hadn't* mentioned was the fact that zeolite contains aluminum.

I felt the hairs on my arms stand on end as a shiver rippled through my body. *How can I, in good conscience, give my son something that has already damaged him?*

One study reported that zeolite clinoptilolite has more silica than aluminum in it. The author went on to state that zeolite clinoptilolite is a very good chelator, binding to soft metals such as mercury, aluminum and lead, while leaving vital vitamins and minerals intact in the body.[13]

But knowing that there was still aluminum in zeolite clinoptilolite made me hesitant in giving it. I nixed the idea of the zeolite and turned my attention to chlorella and cilantro, instead.

I found out that chlorella is considered to be one of the best superfoods in the world, replete with amino acids, essential fatty acids, B-12 and vitamins and minerals. It's also a powerful chelator of neurotoxins, including heavy metals and toxic chemicals, as well as being an anti-bacterial and anti-viral. It binds with the heavy metals in the bowels and carries it out through the feces. Cilantro is more effective at mobilizing the neurotoxins from the cell membranes than actual chelation, but, combined with chlorella, makes for a potent chelator of heavy metals and other neurotoxins. [14]

That weekend when Luke and I made our weekly run to the health food store, I asked the salesgirl about chlorella and cilantro as a detoxifier, and if the store sold them. She told me about NDF Plus, which, she stated, contains both chlorella and cilantro in a dropper form, and was both dairy and gluten-free. She told me that she took a dropper-full every day and didn't have any side effects from it. She said that I would have to order it online, as their store didn't carry it.

I rushed home and looked up the NDF Plus. The more I read about it, the more excited I became, convinced that I had found a chelator effective against heavy metals, but safe enough to take every day, as it doesn't deplete the body of essential vitamins and minerals. I also read that NDF Plus is excreted through the urine as opposed to the feces, decreasing the possibility of reabsorption of the heavy metals through the bowels. [15]

I frowned, though, when I saw the cost. According to the online store where I had to order it, a month's supply of NDF Plus was fifty dollars. But I rationalized that repeat visits to the doctor and the cost of DMSA, as well as the potential damage to the body, was a lot more than fifty dollars a month, so I hit the "buy now" button for a three-month supply, and hoped for the best.

A week later the NDF Plus showed up on our doorstep. It came in dropper form, just like the salesgirl at the health food store had said. It was very easy for Luke to take, and he tolerated it very well; no more having to plead with him to take his medicine.

We continued the NDF Plus for the next year. Over the course of that year Luke appeared calm and his attention span and memory were sharp. His speech wasn't always clear, though, and he walked on his toes and paced the floors a lot.

One day I went to reorder Luke's NDF Plus. As I hit the order button, by accident I somehow magnified the ingredients label. A chill raced down my spine as the word lacti jumped out at me.

With trembling fingers, I looked up the manufacturer's website and called the number listed. After I got a person on the phone, I asked if there was dairy in the NDF Plus.

A woman answered in a pleasant voice that though the NDF Plus was made in a dairy base, they didn't detect any milk proteins in their product when they tested it.

I felt my heart thud as a feeling of dread flooded my body. "*Dairy-based!*" I bellowed. "Why isn't it on the label that it's dairy-based? That means it has dairy in it!"

I slammed down the phone and turned a woeful eye to Luke, who had stopped in mid-pacing and stared at me as if I had come undone.

"I'm so sorry, Luke, but I didn't do my research well enough," I whispered. "That NDF Plus has dairy in it, so we have to stop using it." I choked on a sob. "I've been giving you something that hasn't been good for you, and I'm so very sorry for that."

I grabbed one of his hands and placed it against my cheek, which was damp with tears. "Can you ever find it in your heart to forgive me?"

Luke nodded once and touched my hair. That one gesture spoke more to me than a thousand words ever would.

I sniffled and smiled through my tears. "Time to go back to the ole drawing board. Maybe we should take the doctor's advice this time and give the zeolite a go. We'll monitor you closely, and if you appear to become toxic again, we'll stop it. What say you, little buddy?"

Luke grunted and went back on his merry way.

I ordered a three-month supply of the zeolite, which made it cheaper, being careful to get the one with the clinoptilolite, as that kind allegedly has less aluminum in it. I gave Luke one of the capsules every morning, which he tolerated with no apparent side effects.

I also took this time to work on Luke's speech. I found a qualified speech therapist who was able to extract better communication from him. We also worked on telephone etiquette, which was something Luke had always struggled with. I would have him call and make his own appointments and requests. It was difficult for Luke at first, and the person on the receiving end of the phone had a hard time understanding him, requiring me to intervene. But as his speech progressed via his therapist, he became more confident in speaking on the phone; thus better understood by other people, making gigantic strides towards independence for him.

One month after starting the zeolite, my phone pinged, indicating a text message. I felt a pang stab my heart as I stared at the sender's name. *Gary, how could you have abandoned us when we needed you the most?* I swiped the tears that had clouded my vision and read the message.

"Luke called me last night and sounded good ... shockingly good. So ..."

Leave it to Gary to come a-calling after the home fires have been put out, I fumed to myself. But then I thought about Luke having the courage to reach out to his dad after years of neglect, and put my anger aside.

"So ... what?" I texted back.

My phone pinged immediately. 'So, I don't know what you've done to Luke, but he's never talked to me before. I would like for him to stay with me this weekend, and maybe we can start over again as a family."

I felt my gut wrench as I read the words I had longed to hear for so long. I took a deep breath and steadied my fingers as I typed the words that would seal our fate.

"It's too late for you and I, but just the beginning for you and Luke."

Chapter 16

Winds of change swirled into the valley of the North Georgia mountains. Luke graduated from middle school with minimal issues. He continued on his zeolite and maintained his gluten-free/dairy-free/sugar-free diet. But best of all, he had the relationship with his dad that he had always yearned for.

As Luke got better and required less care, I decided that this was the time to take care of myself a bit. The first thing I did was to contact a lawyer and proceed with the divorce that I had put off for years, having focused all of my time and energy on getting Luke well. I moved Luke and myself out of the monstrosity that had started all of Luke's problems and into a small house close to the high school that Luke would be attending.

I then joined a gym, and worked out every day to quell the anger that lingered inside of me. I forced myself to forgive Gary, though the demon that sat on my shoulder kept reminding me that he didn't deserve forgiveness, and that I should continue to be angry at him. I squashed that demon by repeating to myself that the forgiveness was for my mental health, not for Gary.

After I got my head back on straight, I quit working for Gary. Instead, I got a job at the local hospital, so that I could free myself both emotionally and financially from my ex-husband.

Luke's high school years flew by. Before I knew it, my child was standing on the podium receiving his diploma, while I sat in the audience squalling like a baby.

Then, against all odds and my wildest expectations, Luke went to college. The day he crossed the stage and accepted his bachelor degree in computer science was the proudest day of my life; a day I thought I would never see, and according to most, a day that would be impossible to achieve. He stood up there on center stage, grinning like a cat and waving his diploma high in the air as if saying *I did it!*

Tears coursed down my cheeks as the sorrowful years that preceded this glorious moment flashed through my mind: Luke's traumatic birth, his twin dying, his dad's rejection of him and subsequent abandonment of his family, talk of placing Luke in an institution, the kids' bullying, the near-death experiences. Somehow, Luke's managed to forgive the sins of his childhood and has grown into adulthood unscathed from bitterness and anger. He's the strongest person I've ever had the honor of knowing, and I simply adore him.

As Luke tossed his cap towards the skies, I jumped out of my chair and yelled, "We did it, little buddy!"

At that moment, I felt a stirring, as if a kiss had brushed my cheek. I looked up at the heavens and whispered, "Thanks for saving your brother. You're always in my heart."

* * *

Is Luke perfect? Not by any stretch of the imagination. He still has his quirks, which makes him the unique, funny person whom I love so dearly. But if he stays on his diet and his zeolite, he's indiscernible from his typically-developed peers.

Luke got a job soon after graduation and moved into his own apartment in the big city, fulfilling a life-long dream of being independent and free. Most important of all, though, he's grown into a happy, healthy, productive member of society.

And, in the end, isn't that what we want for *all* of our kids, autistic or not?

The five things I would do when I first suspected something was wrong with my child

1. Early intervention is crucial.

My son missed all of his milestones. He wasn't cooing and smiling at his two-month well-baby check-up, and he wasn't babbling and watching my face at four months. He was stiff as the proverbial board when I tried to cuddle him, and he never smiled, made eye contact with me or pointed. But back then, because autism wasn't as prevalent as it is now, doctors weren't screening for autism at a younger age.

Nowadays, pediatricians use the M-CHAT chart, or modified checklist for autism in toddlers, to look for missing milestones between the ages of 16 and 30 months, that may signify developmental delays. Or you can go to *m-chat.org* and answer a 20-question survey, submit it and receive feedback as to the status of your child's developmental milestones.

The CDC also has a website, *cdc.gov/concerned*, which has a milestones checklist, as well as a milestones app that tracks your child's milestones; something that you can share with your pediatrician. This website also advises parents on what to do if they suspect that their child is developmentally delayed; namely, to ask their pediatrician for a referral to a developmental pediatrician, child neurologist, child psychologist or psychiatrist. These professionals can start services in the critical first two years of life, when the brain is thought to be the most adaptive to learning. ABA (applied behavior analysis,) speech, occupational and physical therapy are some of the services offered, aimed at minimalizing developmental delays.

Luke didn't get his autism label until he was three years old. If we had caught it at an earlier age, we could have determined what was causing his autistic symptoms, and treated it at an age much earlier than we ended up doing. The bottom line is, the earlier we correct the insult to the brain, the more likely the success towards an independent life as an adult will be.

2. Get genetic testing.

There was no talk of genetics causing autism when Luke was a baby, so I wasn't privy to this tool back then. Genetic testing didn't become available until after the Human Genome Project, a 13-year corroboration of scientists around the world who banded together to develop a genetic blueprint of the human body. This remarkable feat paved the way for medical genetic testing, or microarray analysis, which began around the mid-2000s.

There are several companies that do microarray testing. Some of them are direct-to-the-consumer, like 23andme, and involves a saliva test. The price the last time I checked was around $99, and is not covered by insurance since it's not considered a medical genetic test. From my understanding, the reason these tests are so inexpensive is because they can become open records, which means that government agencies, researchers and pharmaceutical companies can have access to the results.

Then there are microarray tests that the doctor may order. These tests cost considerably more than the direct-to-consumer, but are kept private between the provider and the guardian of the child, and should be covered under your insurance.

As it stands now, researchers have not isolated a gene that causes autism. They have discovered several genes that may make a child at a higher risk for autism, such as MTHFR variants C677T or A1298C. Being negative or positive for the MTHFR variants, though, doesn't mean that you have or don't have autism.

So why get medical genetic testing for your child if there isn't a definitive autism gene? For starters, your doctor will be able to rule out Fragile X, which is a genetic disorder that can cause intellectual disabilities as well as physical developmental delays. Finding a genetic reason for your child's developmental delays can help get your child much needed services. It can also identify underlying medical risks associated with the gene mutation, such as diabetes and heart disease, thus, decreasing morbidity. Medical genetic testing can also prevent unnecessary tests and surgeries, as well as facilitate family planning.

Luke ended up testing negative for the MTHFR gene. I had him tested by a holistic doctor for this particular gene because of my theory that he was genetically pre-disposi-tioned to hold onto heavy metals, instead of excreting them like the body is intended to do. From what I read, the MTHFR gene is very important for methylation, which aids in detoxi-fication. But because Luke tested negative for the MTHFR variant, I had to look at other possible genetic mutations, such as APOE4, which is the gene mutation associated with Alzheimer's.

Which leads me to the two biggest things I wish I had done at an earlier age for my son:

3 .Find a qualified doctor who understands environmental toxins and how to get rid of them.

Something was very wrong with Luke from the moment he was born, rushed into our world by his dying twin. And the fact that his twin was badly damaged and didn't survive birth should have been a major clue that something medical was causing Luke's autistic symptoms. I followed the tradi-tional path and took Luke to pediatricians, then to ear and speech specialists, since he didn't talk. I also got him started in ABA and occupational therapy after he received his autism diagnosis.

Nothing helped. Luke remained mute and oh, so hyper.

It wasn't until Luke's occupational therapist stepped in and recommended a doctor who practiced alternative medicine that Luke began to talk. Alternative medicine is medical treatments that are outside the traditional therapies. I realize that alternative medicine is controversial, and that the AMA (American Medical Association) frowns upon alternative methods of treatments for autism; I recently read an article that the AMA recommends only using a traditional doctor, with the accepted therapies (ABA, speech, occupational and physical therapy,) and to use medications to treat behavioral issues as directed by a qualified doctor.

But sometimes our autistic kids have problems that don't respond to traditional therapies unless their underlying issues are resolved. Kids with GI disturbances, such as chronic diarrhea or constipation, or burdened with heavy metals trapped in their soft tissues, need to get these morbidities treated before they can respond favorably to traditional therapies.

And there is a good possibility that some of the child's autistic tendencies will be reduced, or even eliminated, with heavy metals detoxification. Autistic behaviors such as language deficits, social withdrawal, GI and sleep problems, low muscle tone and decreased attention span are also indicative of heavy metal toxicity.

I didn't find out that Luke had heavy metals toxicity until he was seven years old. We had done blood testing for lead when he was around two years old, but by that time the lead had been absorbed into the soft tissues of his body, so it wasn't detected by a simple blood test. Based on his negative lab, his pediatrician concluded that he didn't have heavy metals toxicity, and closed the book on that discussion. I didn't realize at the time that a heavy metal challenge is the best way to determine whether there are heavy metals stored in the body.

I took Luke to an environmental doctor when it finally dawned on me that our farm was making him sick, and is most likely what killed his twin. The doctor took one look at my son and declared that he was toxic, not autistic. He ordered a heavy metal challenge, which involved giving a chelator (DMSA; a very powerful substance that pulls heavy metals from soft tissues, but still very controversial.) We found out that Luke had a heavy burden of mercury, aluminum, lead and arsenic stored in his body, most notably in his brain via a SPECT (single-photon computerized tomography) scan. By this time, though, the metals had done a lot of damage to his organs. If I had found out as soon as he started displaying aberrant behavior at a much younger age, we could have started treatment much sooner and avoided some of the subsequent damage. It's debatable as to what age the brain loses its elasticity and therefore, cognitive training. But studies have shown that the earlier the intervention, the better the outcome.

4. Space vaccines.

I'm not saying that vaccines cause autism, and I'm not saying don't vaccinate your kids. But giving five vaccines at a time to a baby with a compromised detoxification pathway can be an insult to the child's developing brain. Though mercury has been taken out of most childhood single-dose vaccines, most of them still contain aluminum, which is used as an adjuvant to help the vaccine work better. The CDC (Centers for Disease Control) acknowledges that there is aluminum in vaccines, but goes on to say that the amount is negligible, and that the child will get more aluminum from the environment than from the actual vaccine. But to a child who is genetically predisposed to hold onto heavy metals, five vaccines at one time, combined with environmental aluminum and other toxins, may cause more of a burden of heavy metals than the body can excrete. This, in turn, may cause the body to store the heavy metals in the brain, manifesting itself as autistic traits.

That's why I propose to space vaccines for vulnerable children; no more than one aluminum-containing vaccine at a time, and to detoxify after each vaccine. This would be especially crucial for children with a known family history of autism, AD/HD (attention deficit/hyperactivity disorder,) or for children whom exhibit developmental delays.

During my research, I found a vaccine schedule that is geared towards minimizing aluminum insult to the body. It's called the Dr. Paul Thomas Vaccine-Friendly Plan (VFP.) The VFP calls for no-aluminum Hib vaccines (Acthib) to be given at the same time as either low-dose aluminum DTaP (Daptacel,) or PVC13, and to delay giving the Hep A and Hep B vaccinations. Therefore, with the VFP schedule, only one aluminum-containing vaccine would be given at a time. The child would end up getting most of their childhood vaccines, as required by the CDC, but would only be getting 1820 micrograms of aluminum at the end of their 18-month schedule, as opposed to 4925 micrograms with the CDC 2019 schedule.

For detoxifying, I have my son taking zeolite clinoptilolite, which, in hindsight, I wish I had started him on in the very beginning. Zeolite clinoptilolite is a naturally-occurring silica found in the earth's crust, with proven detoxification qualities. Zeolite in its original state is full of aluminum, but zeolite clinoptilolite has been stripped of most of its aluminum. Also, zeolite clinoptilolite is alleged to be excreted from the kidneys instead of the colon, cutting down on the possibility of reabsorption and Herxheimer's (die-off) reaction. It also excretes only toxins and heavy metals, leaving crucial vitamins and minerals intact in the body, as opposed to DMSA and EDTA, which are powerful, but controversial, chelators that pull out both toxins and valuable minerals.

Zeolite comes in dropper, spray and pill form, and is reputed to be safe for all ages. I started Luke on the pill form, and within days his brain fog was gone and his speech was indiscernible from his typically-developing peers. His anxiety also vanished, and his hyperactivity became non-existent. I plan on keeping him on a daily maintenance dosage for the rest of his life.

Disclaimer: I am in no way a medical provider, and am not advising anyone to put their child on zeolite clinoptilolite. A qualified medical provider should be consulted before starting your child on any kind of chelator, especially babies. Be forewarned, though, that many traditional doctors may scoff at the suggestion of chelators in any form, or tout the dangers of it. It took taking my son to a holistic doctor, who prescribed zeolite; hence, leading my son down that elusive path towards a lifetime of health, happiness and independence.

5. Dairy-free/Gluten-free (DFGF) diet.
A lot of kids on the autism spectrum have GI disturbances similar to irritable bowel syndrome (IBS.) Symptoms such as diarrhea, abdominal pain and constipation follow these kids around like a menacing shadow.

They also have yeast overgrowth, many times secondary to taking antibiotics for chronic ear infections. Yeast overgrowth can contribute to leaky gut syndrome, which is increased intestinal permeability, allowing harmful bacteria and toxins to be leaked through the intestinal wall into the bloodstream, causing food sensitivities, autoimmune and mood disorders. Leaky gut is for the most part shunned by the traditional medical community, though, and is not a considered a recognized medical diagnosis.

Gluten and dairy proteins have been shown to cause GI disturbance in children on the autism spectrum, which may lead to social, cognitive and speech deficits. The theory is that the body processes the proteins and peptides in these foods differently than in non-autistic people, causing the child to exhibit autistic traits.

Luke had raging diarrhea, alternating with constipation. I did not remove dairy and gluten from his diet until he was around ten years old, but only after a holistic doctor told me that I needed to. This is another thing that I wish I had done at an earlier age. But, because he didn't test as being allergic to these foods, I didn't think that the DFGF diet would help him. And the thought of yanking his beloved pizza from him broke my heart. I just couldn't do that to him, when he was already suffering so much.

But the doctor assured me that removing dairy and gluten from his diet would help his GI tract heal, therefore, easing his suffering. The doctor went on to say that there is delicious pizza that is completely dairy and gluten-free, and that my son would love it.

The doctor was so right. Around three months after we removed dairy and gluten from Luke's diet, and added a dairy-free probiotic of at least 30 billion CFUs (colony forming units) and 10 different strains, his bowels began to normalize for the first time in his life. He also stopped stimming and walking on his toes.

And Luke was very happy with his DFGF pizza.

It wasn't easy removing all dairy and gluten from Luke's diet. We started with the removal of dairy, which wasn't terribly difficult once we found his dairy-free cheese and chocolate rice milk. The gluten was a lot harder to tackle, as we found out that gluten is pervasive in the American diet. We learned to read labels, though, and after we got used to it, it wasn't hard at all to maintain.

We also had to remove high fructose from Luke's diet, as sugar caused IBS in him. It also contributed to his leaky gut, since sugar feeds yeast. It took us a while to figure out that ketchup gave him incontinent diarrhea, which was a huge source of embarrassment for him. We discovered that products made with the sugar substitute stevia was safe for him to eat, and did not raise his glycemic index (blood sugar.)

Luke knows that he must be diligent in watching his intake of sugar for the rest of his life if he wants to avoid triggering his IBS. But he has learned to accept this; he's realized that a few seconds of sugary bliss is not worth a lifetime of gastro-intestinal misery.

I realize that the DFGF diet is controversial, and it may not help every autistic child, but it has helped my son tremendously. A lot of the damage to his GI tract was most likely from heavy metals when he was born, as his twin had a severe bowel obstruction. So, removing the foods that he was sensitive to helped heal his GI tract, and the removal of sugar killed the yeast lurking in his body, as well as his IBS.

Hopefully, scientists will discover the definitive cause of autism, and this heartbreaking disorder will be eradicated; at least, for the severely affected. Who knows, maybe they'll realize that a lot of what was labeled autism was actually heavy metal toxicity, especially those labeled as being high-functioning autism.

Until that day comes, though, the steps we take to reduce our child's autistic behaviors may be the difference between a lifetime of heartache, or a fruition into adulthood as a happy, healthy, independent and productive member of society.

About the Author

Scarlett South is a registered nurse specializing in autism, a contributor to *Autism Parenting* magazine and author of *Autistic or Toxic? How I Unlocked the Mystery of My Son's "Autism."* But her proudest achievement  is her awesome son, who started out in life labeled as being severely autistic, and who is now an independent and productive member of society. Scarlett is based in Florida.

References

1. Kanner's Syndrome. The Free Dictionary by Farlex

2. Treffert, D. *The savant syndrome: an extraordinary condition. A synopsis: past, present, future.* Philos Trans R Soc Lond B Biol Sci. (2009 May 27)

3. Barrett M.D., S. *Richard E. Layton, M.D. Banned from Using Chelation Therapy.* Casewatch (May 21, 2015)

4. Rudy, L. *Why the Defeat Autism Now (DAN!) Protocol Was Discontinued.* Verywell health. (March 25, 2020)

5. Sears, M. *Chelation: Harnessing and Enhancing Heavy Metal Detoxification-A Review.* Scientific World Journal (April 18, 2013)

6. *Deaths Associated with Hypocalcemia from Chelation Therapy—Texas, Pennsylvania, and Oregon, 2003—2005.* CDC. MMWR Weekly. (March 3, 2006)

7. Newman, T. *How inflammation and gut bacteria influence autism.* Medical News Today. (April 21, 2018)

8. Ruzbarsky, J. *Toe walking: causes, epidemiology, assessment, and treatment.* Curr Opin Pediatr. (2016 Feb; 28)

9. MHadjivassiliouMRCP[a]AGibsonPhD[a]G.A.BDavies-JonesMD[a]A.JLoboMD[b]T.JStephensonMD[c]AMilford-WardFRCPath[d]. *Does cryptic gluten sensitivity play a part in neurological illness?* The Lancet. (February 10, 1996)

10. *The Human Genome Project.* Genome.gov/human-genome. (October 7, 2019)

11. Elif Funda Sener, , * Didem Behice Oztop, and Yusuf Ozkul. *MTHFR Gene C677T Polymorphism in Autism Spectrum Disorders.* Genet Res Int. (November 6, 2014)

12. McCaulley, M. *Autism spectrum disorder and mercury toxicity: use of genomic and epigenetic methods to solve the etiologic puzzle.* Acta Neurobiol Exp (Wars). 2019

13. Sandra Kraljević Pavelić,[1,*] Jasmina Simović Medica,[2] Darko Gumbarević,[1] Ana Filošević,[1] Nataša Pržulj,[3] and Krešimir Pavelić[1], *Critical Review on Zeolite Clinoptilolite Safety and Medical Applications in vivo.* Frontiers in Pharmacology. (November 27, 2018)

14. McLure, M. *Dosing with Chlorella/Cilantro for Neuro-toxin Elimination.* National Integrated Health Associates

15. Kaslow, M.D., J. *NDF Mier Chelating Drops*

Made in the USA
Las Vegas, NV
04 March 2021

19001050R00085